Beyond Two Rivers

Beyond Two Rivers

Hugh Rogers

Independently published

Print layout, e–book conversion, and cover design by DLD Books
Editing and Self–Publishing Services
www.dldbooks.com

Cover image by Jim Black from Pixabay

ISBN: 978-1-7345963-0-4

For Monique

and for the rivers

"Only that day dawns to which we are awake."

—Henry David Thoreau

Chapter 1

I decided to stop for coffee.

After getting pulled over and searched by the Mounties, it was time for a break. Coffee stops were a way to shake the boredom of the drive and get our blood moving again, though this one was more for the relief it provided, and the sleepy atmosphere in the restaurant was welcome. The dim lighting matched the grimy floor. Waitresses shuffled slowly this late, serving plates of hash to truckers and others on night shifts. The customers mumbled, if they spoke at all. The soundtrack of clinking utensils and murmuring combined with the cigarette smoke drifting over the tables.

Fiddling with a sugar packet at the restaurant's counter, I took a sip of coffee and asked my younger brother, "So, Ben, how would you like to drive for a while?"

I'm not sure where that question came from, but I'd been stewing over his stash of marijuana and how close the search we'd just been through had come to landing us in jail. The penalties were harsh—a friend of mine in Vermont was serving two years in jail for possession of not much more than Ben carried. Here in Canada the law was even stricter. I figured that if he had a more active involvement in the trip, he'd realize the risk pot created and get rid of it.

I'd done all the driving so far and was beginning to feel like a parent, which was largely my fault. As the elder, I'd always tried to be the big brother. When Ben's father divorced our mother, I wasn't living at home, and I felt like I needed to fill in with some kind of role model. But I wasn't sure what I should model and hadn't had a model myself. Besides, Ben had a direction of his own that I didn't feel right interfering with.

So when I visited him at home, we played baseball or went fishing, or any of the other usual things two brothers did together. I also exercised my fledgling paternal instinct. I bought him his first rifle, a .22, and showed him how to shoot and clean it. I was trying to provide for him what I'd been without. Maybe I was trying too hard.

I was aware of my responsibility for the unequal relationship, and now I needed a friend and compatriot in adventure more than I needed to be a father figure. Just 21 myself, I was now looking for other young men to share this new stage in life with. The idea of being a guide for Ben just didn't fit anymore.

What I really wanted to feel now was more like two brothers seeking their holy grail together. So what if he was only 15 years old and didn't have a license.

"Look," I said. "I'm tired and I'd like to get some sleep. But if we could make it to Calgary a couple of days before Tim's plane arrives, we'd have time to scout the area. It's a straight road without much traffic, and the weather is good. We just got stopped and searched, so it's very unlikely that'll happen again anytime soon. You could just wake me up when you've had enough."

I knew he was tempted, but his knit brow said he was nervous, too. He spun on his stool to face me, his nail-bitten fingers drumming on the counter. His black tee shirt draped his thin frame, and his sleepy brown eyes looked sincere.

"It's okay with me if it's really okay with you. I might not be able to see over the dashboard, but I could probably solve that with a pillow."

"Sounds good to me," I said.

And on our way out, I pilfered a few extra sugar packets for good luck. This had become our way to restock condiments and seasonings. If we were running low on sugar, we'd just help ourselves to a few extra packets of whatever was offered free to customers.

We didn't think of it as stealing. To us, it was stretching our budget. We hadn't started with a huge wad of money and didn't know how long we'd be gone. We just figured we'd spend about half of what we had and head home from wherever we were. If we could make that first half last longer, then we could get farther, see more, and fish more. We told ourselves we were conserving our resources.

Ben's father had been shorter than mine, and our genes were reflected in our heights. But the bench seat of the Plymouth slid forward enough for Ben to reach the gas and the brake pedals, and the pillow propped him enough to see comfortably over the hood.

"There's not that much to it, really, Ben," I said, pointing out the automatic's shift buttons. "You're only going to be in drive anyway, but there's neutral and reverse if you need them."

"How about the lights?" he asked.

"The knob is here. Pull all the way out for headlights, and the floor button is for the high and low beams. The parking brake lever is on your left, under the dash."

He tried each of these controls, released the parking brake, and gently let the car roll back while idling, carefully looking in all directions for clearance. He was cautious entering the highway and gradually brought the car up to speed, testing the steering wheel for response and getting used to the size of the vehicle.

The cool evening air rushed through the open windows, and with his long red hair swirling around his head, Ben turned to me, his face beaming, and said, "This is a gas!"

Slapping him a high five, I replied, "Right on, bro! What's it like?" I asked.

"The car feels huge. It's solid everywhere, with a monster engine and lots of momentum. I'm counting on the brakes to stop this puppy," he replied, with caution in his voice.

They're good," I assured him. "We had the brake shoes and drums checked just before we left. They don't grab. Easy pressure will brake the car smoothly. How is it for you?"

"I'm used to the ride, but I've got to pay attention. No more staring out the window and spacing out." He was looking straight through the windshield as he spoke.

"It'll get easier with practice. It's a good sign you're this comfortable first time at the wheel. My own wasn't too smooth," I said, trying to help him relax.

"No?" he asked.

"I drove a fifty–six Chevy wagon with a three–speed on the column over the soccer field up at the school. It was a weekend with no one around. I struggled timing the clutch and the gas pedal, and the car bucked like a bronco down the field, stalling the engine a few times. I was terrified I'd crash into the goal posts. But I got the hang of it quick enough and got to like that car."

Ben had settled in a bit and was glancing at me once in a while as I spoke.

"I'm breathing a little easier now," he said. "Not so white knuckle."

"Glad to hear it. Let me know if you have any questions."

"Sure thing. Steady as she goes, for now," he said.

Without a steering wheel or a centerline in front of me for the first time in over 2,000 miles, I was free to look around and absorb the panorama of the prairie under a moonlit night. I relaxed completely and within no time was ready to crawl in the back and doze. Ben seemed like he had settled in.

"You mind if I catch a few zzs?" I asked.

"Just do me a favor first and roll me some cigarettes, eh?" he asked. I quickly rolled him a small stack of smokes and crawled into the back. Just lying down was such a relief that I fell asleep instantly.

It must have been a deep sleep too, because the next thing I remember was the stabbing flashes of revolving lights bouncing off the ceiling of the Plymouth.

I sat bolt upright, saw the cruiser in the distance behind us, turned and caught sight of Ben's face in the rear-view mirror, eyes wide open, jaws clenched, every feature tense. The Royal Canadian Mounted Police, as the national police in Canada, are tough and uncompromising, a demeanor we'd already experienced earlier in the evening. With all the control I could gather I asked Ben, "Were you speeding?"

"No, I don't think so" came as a slight relief.

"Look, it's probably just another spot check, but if they catch you driving, we're screwed. Quick, switch with me." I flipped over the seat, reached behind Ben's shoulder, took the wheel, and let him scoot out over my lap. The car began to slow and I pulled it over and gradually brought it to a stop.

Instantly, both officers were out of their cruiser and running to our open windows with huge flashlights. Pointing his beam right in Ben's eyes, one officer barked, "I need to see your license. I bet you don't have one, do you? I saw you make that switch."

At my shoulder, so close I could see the pores on it, was the other officer's face. Then the face said, "You boys need to slowly step out of the car now."

The face was twitching, and the head it was attached to was shaking back and forth, along with the stiff brim of the hat on top of it. The vibrations from all these sources, combined with the spinning red beams and the flashlight rays, produced a ghastly effect. Then the teeth in the face curved into a leer and snarled, "Right now."

And while we huddled on the side of the road, the two Mounties turned the car inside out, searching for something they were sure they'd find. When their efforts didn't pay off right away, they moved to the trunk. There, they asked us to unwrap every food item or cooking implement that had a possible hiding spot. They were especially particular when they opened the tackle boxes because they were crammed with small containers of all sorts, holding lures, split shot, snap swivels, and other fishing tackle. We'd long ago developed the habit of separating different hook sizes into bundles wrapped in foil, and they opened those. They turned each sleeping bag inside out, unpacked our tent and shook it out, and turned our backpacks upside down and shook them. What had been neatly organized storage was now a landfill.

By this time, Ben and I were chilled, standing with hunched shoulders, our hands in our pockets. One of the officers noticed this and a light must have come on in his head because he quickly moved toward me and demanded, "Show me your hands." I slowly withdrew my hands from my pockets, afraid for a moment he thought I had a knife, but knowing, too, what he was really looking for. After I turned my hands over he said to Ben, "Now you."

I could feel the lump in my throat begin to rise and choke me, as all eyes turned to Ben's hands, now unfolding in the flashlight's beam. “Oh no,” I thought, “we're headed for jail.” But like a magic trick, the marijuana I'd envisioned was gone. Nothing. The lump receded and I began to breathe again.

"Shouldn't take you more than a few minutes to put your belongings back together," one of the Mounties said. "Then you can be on your way." And pointing at me, he added, "With *you* driving." Then they marched to their cruiser, turned off the flashing red lights, and roared off into the night.

While the shock receded, Ben and I gaped at each other in the light from passing headlights.

"So Ben, where was it, anyway?" I finally asked.

"In my pocket. If he'd asked me to empty them, we'd be on our way to Her Majesty's hoosegow right now."

“Hell of a first time at the wheel, Ben. You okay?” I asked.

“I'm all right, but I don't feel like driving right now.” He smiled and shivered. "What do you say we get this mess cleaned up enough to close the trunk and figure out the details in the morning?"

"Sounds good to me. Oh, and by the way, do you know what

you catch in Sas–*katch*–e–wan?"

"No. What?" Ben asked.

"Nothing, Ben. Absolutely nothing."

"Well, this is the first time I've been truly happy catching nothing."

"Me too, bro. Me too."

Chapter 2

This was the summer of 1972, when I took a journey with my two brothers, Ben and Tim, across North America and as far north as you could then go by car.

Our journey was shaped by the dynamics among us a long way from home, together for the first time in eight years, and an even longer way from the comforts and routines we knew. As kids, whenever home life had gotten too rough, we lit out for our sanctuary, the rivers and fields away from the war. And when that conflict finally broke us up, those rivers became the lifelines through which we remained connected. They carried us to worlds where discovery only revealed itself to the watchful eye, the welcoming heart, and the peaceful soul. There we found treasures: the reassurance of motion, companionship, and solitude, all strengthened by the trials we encountered.

Some people seek their identity in family trees, but what we had come to realize was that the trees in the forest, along with the hills, the meadows, and especially the rivers, had become our family. So we went to the wilderness. And wilderness for us had always pointed north.

Wilderness became a repository for us. More than merely an escape, it became the framework against which we measured the drunken incoherence of our domestic life. At a time in our lives when we needed a family greatly, at that point in every young man's life when he's asking himself where his true directions lay, we turned to the direction we knew: the wild. And the wildest place we knew was Alaska.

None of this was conscious. If you had asked us at the time, we were going for the fishing that we'd read about and seen in magazines for years. The fish weren't just bigger; there were more of them, lots more. And all of them were wild. There were no scrawny, pasty–fleshed, hatchery–raised fish like those at home. Their abundance tested our environmental conscience. It also gave us a penetrating experience in just how incredibly bountiful the pure, unadulterated wilderness was. It was sickening to suddenly realize so viscerally that this volume of life was once the rule everywhere, and how seriously our species had impoverished our spiritual lives in pursuit of material progress.

This was in the days before computers and cell phones, when pay phones and collect calls were the emergency lifelines to home. But they were expensive, and mostly we mailed postcards or letters, knowing that, on the move, we sent our narratives one way, without expecting anything coming back.

Perhaps we wrote to let others at home know we were still alive and not to worry, but perhaps we also wrote to assure ourselves that there would be a home to return to when we were done with our road test. And maybe there was even a hope that the home we left would somehow transform itself in our absence into a truly nurturing destination, a place welcoming our return and worthy of our devotion.

The plan was simple: go west and north, hiking and fishing until we had enough or ran out of money, or both. We did ask our older sister, Tamsen, along, but she declined, not without good reason, as it turned out. Accompanying three young men with fire in their eyes was risky. This trip wasn't about reason. It was about challenge, spontaneity, and endurance. It included a penchant for bad behavior and the need to face the result and find a way out of it, by cleverness, luck, or a bottomless well of youthful strength.

There was quite a bit not commonly known about travel in Alaska in 1972. Available information came in the form of a stubby magazine called *The Milepost.* It described the facilities, sights, and activities from the beginning of the Alaska-Canada Highway in Dawson Creek, British Columbia, to Fairbanks, Alaska. And it presented them all with a sense of adventure and plenty of reminders that this trip had more than its share of pitfalls.

The list of hazards was long and novel, which *The Milepost* provided cautions for while downplaying them. The authors were trying to promote tourism, so when they mentioned rough roads, those were very different from what suburbanites had in mind. "Rough roads" could mean a section with potholes the size of pool tables or stretches with washboards that turned your car's suspension into jelly. The authors casually suggested that installation of a grill screen and transparent headlight cones was a good idea. These accessories served to deflect rocks thrown from the wheels of oncoming tractor trailers into, or sometimes through, your windshield or headlights. Later we'd see a few cars that had obviously made the trip, or part of it, without this protection. They were easy to spot: they looked like the last remaining car in the demolition derby.

The Al-Can was just as remarkable for what it didn't have. Service stations to make the inevitable repairs were rare. A particularly lonesome one, deep in the Yukon Territory, had no full service but was a much welcome sight. The "garage," a bedroom-sized plywood shanty where the mechanic kept a few tools and a jack, rose from a roughly cleared patch of forest. He worked on your car outside, on the gravel, where the single hand gas pump stood. For over a hundred miles in either direction there was nothing else, nothing man-made except for the gravel surface of the Al-Can itself. No phone poles, no power lines, no houses or buildings of any kind.

There was no posted speed limit; the road itself limited your speed. In fact, there were no signs at all, from any of the categories you'd studied in your driver's ed text. No diamond-shaped hazard signs, no rectangular regulation signs, no commercial signs, and no billboards. There were no direction signs either. None were needed: there were no turnoffs. It was one of those rare situations in which you couldn't get lost. You were in the middle of nowhere and the middle of everywhere at the same time.

Then there were the subjective hazards that *The Milepost* never mentioned: the psychological and emotional tolls from compulsive driving, stemming from the ever-strengthening conviction that if you didn't keep driving you'd never get there. At the same time you were acutely aware that, precisely because of this distance from home, it was very unlikely that you would ever see what you were passing again in your life. It wasn't boredom. It was the fatigue from extended immersion in another world. The Al-Can experience was of such relentless duration that once you were committed to the drive, turning back didn't seem an option. It became a sense of destiny you were compelled to fulfill.

It seems silly now, in our age of easy air travel, to make so much of just a road. But the Al–Can was the only overland route to Alaska and just getting to the start of it required a cross–continental trek, at least for us. Its remote location was part of its appeal.

It was a 1,5000 mile dirt road, which wound west and north from Dawson Creek through British Columbia and the Yukon Territory into the northern end of the Alaskan Panhandle at Haines Junction and then further north through the interior, where it ended in Fairbanks. There was a small town called Circle about 150 miles northeast of Fairbanks, also on a dirt road, and that was it. Before the Alaska Pipeline dramatically changed the state forever, that was as far north in North America that you could get by car. Even so, you'd still be south of the Arctic Circle, though not by much. That's where we were headed. As far as the details of exactly how and when that would happen, we had the brilliantly conceived plan most men our age would have concocted: put gas in the car and drive.

Chapter 3

Of course we knew this was to be a major trip, but in our innocence we believed it was to be just the first one of many that we would be taking together in search of trout and adventure. Ben, at 15, was the youngest, and had just finished his sophomore year at a private school and was to return in the fall. Tim was 19 and had tried college, but found life as a house painter a better fit. He was finishing a large job and would be flying out to Calgary, Alberta, where Ben and I would pick him up. I was the oldest and had just graduated from college, but other than a vague idea about wanting to teach and write, I had no direction other than to see this land that I'd read about and dreamt of for years.

Alaska: I remember first the pull of the wilderness, but accessibility was key also. You could get there with a car, and you needed one to explore its vast territory. We had all seen pictures of giant trout caught in Argentina and Chile, but flying there was too costly, and driving there presented visions of three gringos getting into serious trouble in unstable places. We were looking for adventure in the wilderness, not in a foreign legal system. As it turned out, going north provided experiences of both kinds. As a friend once said, quoting Yvon Chouinard, "It's not an adventure until something goes wrong."

Through my teens I'd read a magazine about Alaska that

had stories on homesteading and how you got started. One hundred sixty acres was yours if you lived on it for at least six months of the year and within five years had erected a habitable dwelling. It was the free land that got me hooked. As Mark Twain observed: "They're just not making any more of it," and I'd seen it being gobbled by subdivisions at home.

I saw myself as Henry David Thoreau: self-reliant and ready to use all my free time writing the Great American Novel. As a card-carrying transcendentalist I'd listened carefully when Henry advised me to aim high. I figured I could build a cabin with the sources in the *Whole Earth Catalogue* and *Mother Earth News*. I knew I could saw and split enough wood to stay warm, even through the long winter. This was something I actually did have experience at, clearing land for the golf course I worked on during my summers in high school and college. The magazines also described how, by taking one moose, settlers put hundreds of pounds of meat in the freezer. And I didn't need electricity to cool that freezer if I had a propane-powered one.

I'd also read about how, in the long light of the Alaskan summer, farmers grew 100-pound cabbages and other vegetables of Brobdingnagian proportions. The extensive *Whole Earth Catalog*, combined with these resources for shelter, warmth, and food, as well as a healthy complement of hard work, would allow me to meet my needs and give me the time to write.

In addition to all the attractions Alaska offered, there were discomforts that were pushing me from the life I'd known. Growing up in a wealthy suburb of New York City, I'd seen too many men trade their lives for hours riding on a commuter train to a job that consumed them. They spent their weekends at the country club, where they and their wives drank too much. Their children were given everything materially possible but much less that was spiritually necessary, including their parents' time. Teen drug use was rampant. It didn't make any sense. Why strive for all the money and recognition if, in the process, you lost all connection with your family or sense of purpose?

I'd been reading Herman Hesse and Alan Watts and similar authors, and the struggles they described were my own. Hesse taught me there are, indeed, things worse than dying, one of which was dying and never having known who you were. The need to know who I was surfaced on a daily basis from the inner reaches of my consciousness, although I wasn't always hearing it clearly.

Alan Watts taught me that the only path to true happiness was to follow your own way. I wasn't sure what my own way was, but I knew it didn't involve sacrificing my ability to enjoy the present moment for a future that held no guarantees. There were simply too many delicious moments now that demanded awareness. Ignoring them would wilt my soul. There had to be a way to honor your life, not sell it out, and Alaska, I thought, might provide the guidance I was looking for.

Chapter 4

It was the Fourth of July, signs of spring still present in Vermont, when Ben and I rolled out from our mom's house in Weston, headed for the Canadian border, about 150 miles north. I remember thinking, "This is all it took to fulfill a lifelong dream? Pack the car and go?" Then I remembered Goethe: "The world conspires to assist you at the moment of your commitment." Still, it all seemed so uneventful. We could just as easily have been going to the store for milk and bread.

Even our car was unremarkable. A white, nine-year-old Plymouth with 100,000 miles on it was the vehicle of choice. It was either this four-door Belvedere sedan, which belonged to Tim and which he could spare from his collection of cars, or my MG. It would have been hard to pack the peanut butter and jelly alone in the trunk of the MG, never mind the canned foods, boxes of dried foods, backpacking stove, cookware, tent, sleeping bags and mats, clothes, lanterns, flashlights, backpacks and fishing equipment, all neatly stowed in the huge trunk of the Plymouth. There was even room for the spare tire, jack, and lug wrench.

The interior was equally nondescript: bench seats, metal dashboard (including a radio that didn't work), and a journal. This wire-bound notebook started as a ledger of expenses and distances and became the record of events, songs, thoughts, observations and rants, the collective diary.

Other than a few maps on the front seat and the four "new" retread tires we'd had installed in Rutland for a hundred dollars, there were no clues we were about to embark on a road trip the proportions of which we couldn't foresee. One hint, though, might have been that the Belvedere was clean, both inside and out, the cleanest it was to be for the next two months.

It was fitting too that we left on Independence Day. What better way could we have found to affirm our freedom? We pulled out of the driveway and took a left down the hill to the village of Weston, then caught the two–lane state highway north. What other direction?

The route wound along the headwaters of the West River on Route 100, past three lakes north of Ludlow, into the Black River drainage near Plymouth Notch. In West Bridgewater, we crossed the Ottauquechee near its headwaters on Killington Peak, and followed the Tweed River into Pittsfield. Just east of town, the Tweed flows into the White River, one of the longest in Vermont. From there, we paralleled the White River upstream through Rochester, Hancock and Granville, the towns getting smaller going north.

"A lot of sugar houses up here, Ben," I said, spotting the fourth one I'd seen.

"More cold frames and root cellars, too," Ben added, his shoulder length red hair drifting with the breeze.

"Hey, check out that laundry line, sorted by size, from dad down to junior," I said.

"There's some organization," Ben said. "Have you noticed the dogs? No purebreds. They're all mutts."

"And they all look like they've got a job, and they know it," I said.

Ben was the youngest of us three brothers, too young at 15 to drive, which is why I drove until that fateful night. He was also too young to buy cigarettes, so he rolled his own, which he was now doing.

"Hey, roll one for me, will ya?" I asked.

"Sure thing."

We talked to absorb the changes we were encountering, to make plans and mull decisions and to reacquaint ourselves. There were immediate and present topics, but there was also the past, and finding out what each other's life had been like was always in the background. Ben had lived with our mother by himself for the past five years after Tamsen left for private school and then college. Tim and I had left home eight years ago and had had only sporadic contact with either of them.

The big Plymouth floated along under the weight of its cargo and its mission to carry us to the land of our dreams, and back again. Tim, our middle brother, would join us in Calgary, Alberta. While Ben rolled, my mind floated back to when he and I still lived together with Mom. Ben was seven when Tim and I left. I wanted to find out, but wasn't sure where to begin, so I just jumped in.

"So, what's it been like, living with Mom?" I asked. Ben cleared his throat and sat up, blowing smoke out the window.

"Well, I missed you and Tim pretty bad, to be honest. Mom was drunk most of the time, so I was lonely a lot. Sometimes I cried by myself. It was easy to get into pot," he said.

"I feel terrible about not being around for you more, Ben. Tim and I had a rough time at the orphanage in Albany, and then at the foster home with the Boltons across town. No excuse, I know, but I want you to know we missed you, too." Looking for some light, I asked, "What about after junior high, when you moved to Vermont with Mom? Did it get any better then?"

Ben answered as though he'd spent a long time thinking about it. "Mom tried to give me more discipline by sending me to Northfield Mount Hermon School, but I didn't buy the whole prep school thing. No wonder I got booted. She made me feel bad about it too, like I let her down."

"I remember when I drove up to visit you there and they wouldn't let me take you out, even to lunch, because you were on probation," I said.

"I remember that, too. You were the only person that visited me there," he replied.

"Mom didn't come?" I asked.

"Nope."

"Your dean sat me down in his office and went on about how monstrous you'd been. How you'd been repeatedly caught smoking in the dorm, skipping classes and committing other acts of grievous misconduct. Apparently you hadn't been doing all your work either, because he kept referring to your 'selective completion of assignments.' I loved that term. So distant. All to justify your lockdown."

Ben said, "What he didn't know, and never did find out, was that a friend had a car stashed behind a barn close to school, which he and I used to take off on night rides."

"No way!" I said, astonished. "You must have had some adventures on those nights."

"Sure did. Close calls too. Stupid stuff, but nothing destructive. Gags, really. Once, we climbed a church roof at night and speared a pumpkin on the spire. I was scared shitless. We'd drive by for nights afterward and laugh when it was still up there. We asked a few girls to come along, but none were interested. Looking back, I'm glad none of them did."

"Really? How come?" I asked.

"By ourselves, Peter and I just cooked up stupid pranks. If we'd had girls along, we'd have been tempted to show off. Try crazy stuff. You know, drive too fast. Go overboard. Anyway, it all ended one night when we sneaked out to the barn and the car was gone. Peter got word later that his father found out about it and had it removed, without the school knowing. I'll never forget the first thing you said when you came out of your talk with the dean," he said.

"I forget. What did I say?" I asked.

"You said, 'This seems like a good place to leave,'" he replied. "You were so right, I had to laugh. And the dean was standing right behind you. The look on his face was priceless."

"So you've got a year left at the Woodstock School. How's that been so far?" I asked.

"I love it there. Some of my classes and teachers are great. But the rules are so loose we can get away with anything. Smoke pot or listen to music when we should be in class. I'm playing a lot of flute, but I wonder if I'll be ready for college."

"Any school you want to go to?"

"Haven't thought about it."

"Look Ben, I'm really sorry about not being there for you more often."

"I get it. It was a crazy time," he said. "Still is, sort of."

"How's that?" I asked.

"Mom's still drinking and guilt trips me all the time for not helping out more. Wants me around to do stuff for her. It gets old. How about you? What was it like living with the Boltons?"

"Sickening. We never knew when Bill would explode. He'd beat Tim, and Tim would try to stand up to him. Then hell would break loose. I tried to step in, but basically I was chicken. It only ended when Tim returned to live with you at Mom's."

"Did he hit you?" Ben asked.

"Not as much as he hit Tim. I was the "good boy": did my homework, obeyed. Tim stayed out late and his whereabouts were often unknown. This enraged Bill. He'd stew until Tim came home and then start yelling at him. When Tim spoke up, Bill would hit him mercilessly, only stopping when Tim was down. The thing was, Bill himself was a delinquent. He vandalized homes of people he didn't like, shot out streetlights, and lit illegal fireworks at night at the high school. He liked to show off in front of company. He even deliberately crashed a car he owned into a tree to collect on the insurance. I was with him when he did this stuff. He verbally abused his wife, Betty, frequently. And directed that same abuse at me. There was more, too. Personal stuff."

"I sort of guessed at that," Ben said, "but I didn't know how to talk to you about it at the time."

"Tim and I knew our home life there was disturbed. But I was too ashamed to talk about it with anyone. Like if I didn't say anything, it didn't exist. I think Tim felt the same way. Fear of enraging Bill, combined with the shame, kept us both silent. With no outlet, Tim's delinquency was a natural response to Bill's violence, and became a cycle. So Tim and I didn't talk about any of it, which would have helped both of us. Even if I found someone I could talk to, who would believe me? And even if they did believe me, what could they do about it? Sometimes I wished we'd never left home. At least Mom didn't beat us."

"I get it, bro. I get it," Ben said.

Ben was political—he followed the news and took a stand on issues. The civil rights movement, riots in the cities, and assassinations shocked the nation, but the war in Vietnam provided the background for all of them. The anti-war movement surged in 1968, following the My Lai Massacre and massive demonstrations in Washington, D.C. National Guardsmen shot four students demonstrating at Kent State two years later, and in 1971 the Pentagon Papers revealed that President Nixon and Robert McNamara, the Secretary of Defense, had been lying to the public about the war for years. Demonstrators were threatening to disrupt the upcoming Democratic National Convention in Chicago, and authorities there were on tenderhooks. By 1972 over 56,000 G.I.s had died in Vietnam. Some of my friends had enlisted. A couple had moved to Canada.

"Are you afraid of getting drafted?" Ben asked, changing the subject.

"My student deferment will expire soon, and Nixon just ordered a reduction in troop strength by seventy thousand. I'm still eligible for the lottery, but the draft quota will be met with fewer drawn birthdays. There's still a chance, but it's smaller," I replied. "I don't want to move to Canada, but we don't belong in Vietnam."

Ben said, "Well, whatever happens, I hope you aren't drafted."

"Me too," I replied.

In the silence that followed, I thought of Ben back before he was ten, to his horrible accident. He was playing ball in a friend's yard while his friend's Dad was mowing the grass. Intent on catching a fly ball, Ben lost track of the mower, tripped, and his foot slid under the machine. He lost most of his right foot. Months of emotional and physical therapy followed. I'd often wondered how he'd dealt with that.

"What about you, Ben? How has it been dealing with your foot? Since the accident, I've always wondered."

"I can't tell you what a huge bummer it was. I was really depressed for a long time. I still am sometimes. It changed my life in a major way overnight."

"Was counseling a help?" I asked.

"Yeah, Mr. Barrett was a pretty cool guy to talk to. I got the feeling he took me seriously. Sometimes we even laughed about stuff. And your visits were a help. But by myself, I bummed out a lot."

"I'm starting to see how much I missed, buried in my own mess," I said. "But I see now that each of us had our own mess," I continued. "Mom especially. You had your accident. Tamsen was out dating more than she was at home. Tim painted houses, played football, and partied. His parade of cars had everyone wondering, especially the new Chevelle SS 396. I withdrew at the Boltons and sleep-walked my way through high school, clinging to my few friends. Their parents weren't around either."

"Dealing with Mom took most of my attention. We didn't have much left for each other. It's no surprise we weren't connected," Ben said.

"The visits I made to you at Mom's were awkward for me, and maybe for you too. I was always afraid that on those visits you'd ask me to play chess. Even though you were six years younger, you'd beat me more often than not, and I was a sore loser. When I did win, I felt it was because I'd gotten lucky."

"I was afraid you'd blow up and wreck our time together," Ben said. "I just wanted to spend time with you."

"Well, Ben," I said, "if it means anything to you, I'm sorry I was so small about it."

"No problem, bro. Ancient history," he replied.

"I also remember visiting you at Mom's and you'd be in the basement, swinging a bat at the tennis ball hung from the floor joists. You could do that for hours."

"I used to just space out down there by myself. It felt great to really connect with the ball. My Willie Mays fantasy," Ben said.

"You'd also lie on your bed with a speaker at each ear, deep into Herbie Mann. When the song was over, you'd cue it up again and play along with your flute. That blew me away. Amazing talent."

Ben said, "I still have that flute, and those old albums, too. Herbie Hancock, Keith Jarrett, Gentle Giant, Frank Zappa. All incredible."

At Woodstock, Ben skipped classes to play his flute, and developed his own style. He was talented in music, gifted even. He knew theory, could read music, and transposed keys easily. He could play by ear, and would sometimes replay the song we'd just heard as though he'd been practicing it his whole life. He liked rock, but loved jazz and was more devoted to fringe bands than to mainstream ones. I had a hard time understanding some of the music he liked, with its dissonance and nonsyncopated rhythms. With the zeal of a missionary but without the morality, he patiently kept exposing me to higher forms of music. I was his brother, and he felt it his duty to enlighten me. I embraced his intent, but try as I might, I often couldn't fathom his music.

With a broken radio in the car, the rhythms we'd now be moving to would be those the journey imposed or the internal ones each of us carried. As if to test the connection between those two, that rhythm was disrupted right away.

I smelled something burning. "Ben, where's this smoke coming from?"

"Looks like the ashtray. The pile of butts is on fire," he said, laughing.

"I'd better pull over," I said.

"I'd say so. Wouldn't look too good to go down in our home state."

Our first landmark was the Derby Line, the customs checkpoint into Canada. I worried: Ben had a bag of pot on him, but I figured he'd take care of it. We were greeted with the usual questions: Are you traveling on business or pleasure? How long do you plan to stay? Are you carrying any firearms? Do you have any belongings to report? We said plenty about our interest in fishing, hiking, and camping, and that we'd probably be in Canada for a few weeks. For now, that got us through.

From the border the signs for Montreal beckoned, and we were anxious to see this city, which had hosted the 1967 World's Fair with its famous Habitat, the modern housing complex built of cubes. We found something we never expected: a clean, appealing, urban center, a mix of wonderful old architecture and modern, interesting buildings. The signs in French caught our attention. Museums and galleries dotted the downtown.

"Ben, check out the beautiful women on the sidewalks," I

said.

"Some sweet honeys, for sure."

Bilingual signs highlighted restaurants and shops that reflected cultures of the world. We drove through McGill University and gawked at the throngs of urbane students moving between classes.

"No cut-off blue jeans here," Ben said.

"Nope. Definitely sophisticated. Looks sharp," I replied.

"Different nationalities too, also well dressed," he added.

After his dad's divorce from our mother, Ben had ridden the train into New York through Harlem's poverty to visit him in his well-to-do neighborhood downtown. I'd taken the same train to explore the city, through Harlem's street after street of decrepit buildings, some occupied, the occupants, always black, leaning out windows with broken glass, the curtains swaying in the breeze. That poverty found no comparison here. There were no slums. Even the industrial section of Montreal, along the waterfront, was clean and inviting.

"You know, Ben, this looks like a city I could live in. The skies are open, the noise level is okay, and it's clean and interesting."

"I wouldn't mind visiting, if we had the time. Be fun to explore. But I'm looking forward to the wilderness. I want to see a bear in the wild," he replied. So we found signs for Route 117, the Trans-Canada Highway, and pointed the grill towards Mont Tremblant Park.

Chapter 5

Within minutes, road signs reflected the French Catholic history, with many towns named for saints: *Sainte Jerome La Chute*, *Sainte Sophie*, *Sainte Adele*, and *Sainte Agathe-des-Monts*. Ski areas included signs in English as a nod to the U.S., but the English was written under the French. Henri Levesque and the Partie Quebecquois surged in their movement toward an independent Quebec, and the French pride was evident.

Both shop talk and street talk was in French, although residents spoke English for tourists like us without condescension. The Canadians went out of their way to be friendly. They were more relaxed with us, as long-haired youth, than were the adults in our own country.

While we easily found a campsite that night on the shore of Lac Chat in Mont Tremblant Park, we also found the world's proving ground for mosquito repellants. Our chemicals were no match for these wilderness hordes.

"I thought this bug juice had the most active ingredient you could get," Ben said.

"Yeah, but to these flying carnivores it's only a marinade," I replied.

"Oh, I get it. *All* the critters in the north country, not just the fish, are plentiful," he said.

"I think the expression is 'it comes with the territory.'

Staying near the fire helps," I said.

"Then we're going to need more firewood," he said. "I'll get it. There's tangles of it toward the lake."

"Good enough. I'll set up the tent. We're going to need a place to hide."

When he returned, he looked white, even in the firelight, and his hands were shaking.

"I met a black bear. Huge. He walked right past me, where I was gathering wood."

"Are you okay? You look pale," I said.

"Yeah, still spooked though. He surprised me, and vice versa, I think. It's not good to surprise a bear," he said. "I know I wished for it, but from now on, remind me to collect firewood in daylight."

"Will do. Anyway, bears are a sure sign we're in trout country."

We got our first experience with car repair on the road the following day. We drove all morning through the Laurentian Shield, the boreal forest covered with lakes and rivers left by the last Ice Age, 11,000 years ago. The source of the bountiful mosquitoes became obvious: hour after hour we passed through spruce forest, bog, and miles of open water, which was flowing in every direction. The drainages overlapped, with some headed south toward the St. Lawrence and some north toward Hudson's Bay. Many moved toward lakes in the vicinity or from lakes to other lakes.

It was easy to picture crews of voyageurs 150 years ago paddling 25-foot canoes loaded with furs. It was also easy to understand how they became legends in the annals of the north woods. The sheer distances they traveled, usually without rest, are phenomenal.

There were so many lakes and rivers that even with Ben checking the provincial map of Quebec, we lost track of their names. They varied greatly; many lakes stretched to the horizon. Quite a few were many times larger than Lake Champlain, the largest lake in Vermont. Yet we'd never heard of them and even now, with the map out, couldn't keep their French names straight.

The land is so lake and river strewn that Route 117 is still the only road through it. For 250 miles going east and over 100 going west, there are no others. The view out the side window was stroboscopic. Walls of laser–straight black spruce along the roadside were broken with glimmering flashes of open water. Some of the spruce rode horizontally on the behemoth pulp trucks nudging us to the outside. We were tempted to stop at rapids, shouting the presence of huge trout or the deep pools swirling with promise. But the pull to move on was stronger, knowing that our final destination, which held the mythical fish, lay far distant.

About mid–afternoon on our second day, we noticed the Plymouth listing toward the right rear wheel and discovered we had a flat. We changed the tire and drove on to Val–d'Or, where the signs no longer included English and the people didn't speak it. With my high school French (un pneu crevé?) and hand signals, we described our problem to the mechanic, a large, stout man in a beret and worn overalls. He smiled the whole time he repaired the tire. We watched and smiled back as he jammed a rubber plug in the puncture, something we'd never seen before, and remounted it within minutes, still grinning. He took a look at Ben and me and charged us two dollars. We smiled again.

We crossed the border into Ontario two hours later, found a dirt road off the highway, and slept in the car. No tent, no mosquitoes.

Ontario was different from Quebec in more ways than language. The French signs disappeared immediately, as if Canada was trying to contain its Quebecquois upstarts. The topography, still rolling, included many more rivers now than lakes, rivers with long native names: Mettawitchewan, Kabinakagami. Towns appeared at more regular intervals, and we had a stronger sense of being away from home. This province wasn't adjacent to our home state. Route 117 headed north, passing through towns no longer named for saints but for natural features of the landscape: Driftwood, Smooth Rock Falls, and Moonbeam. These weren't names derived from people or events or the cultures they came from. It wasn't just that the French influence had disappeared either, because even the English aspects were muted. With so much of Canada now below us on the map, neither culture mattered that much. The strongest influence here was the natural world, not the human one.

It was getting dark, and we'd just realized we'd lost a headlight when we pulled into Kapuskasing and saw a Mountie gliding along main street in his cruiser.

Wary of being ticketed for our headlight, we found a garage, where the sole employee, a guy about my age, was just closing up. We showed him our headlight, and he cheerily replied in his Canadian accent, "I kin fix that fer ya, no problem. Just pull her inta the bay." Once I did, he shut down all the pumps and outside commercial lights and closed the bay door, even though it was a warm summer night. He kept only one small light on overhead to see his repairs by, and I suddenly became aware that we were now working after hours.

The tone of our exchange shifted from the formality and distance of customer and vendor toward that of compatriots on the road of life. He worked deftly, peppering us with questions in his Canadian English as he replaced the broken lamp.

"I see you're from the States. How far have you come?" he asked.

"We're into our third day. Headed for the Al-Can, in Dawson Creek. Have you been that way? Any advice?" I replied.

"No, I don't get to leave much, with running the station. Went to Ottawa once for my sister's college graduation—that's the furthest. We hear about the protests in the States against the Vietnam War. What's your take on that?" he asked.

"We're with the protesters. The war is a mistake. We shouldn't be in Vietnam," Ben replied, keeping it to the point.

"There's more than a few who agree with you up here," he said.

As he removed the burned out headlight, we leaned in over the engine, relaxed with his cordiality and our sense of connection.

"Okay," he said, "so what I really want to know is—what are the girls really like in the States? From what I read and see on the TV up here, I get the impression they're all beautiful and easy, but I don't believe it."

"You got that right. Actually, they're probably pretty much the same as the girls here. All different. Some nice, some stuck up. Maybe their skirts are a little shorter," I said.

"That's a plus," he said, smiling. "What do you guys do for

fun down there?"

"You know. Party, cruise for babes, listen to music. Probably similar to here," I said.

"Yeah, same as here. But we also hunt and fish a lot," he said. "Those are big around here."

"You're lucky in that department," Ben said. "We're looking for the fishing ourselves. The trunk is loaded with our spinning gear."

"I could show you some good spots around here for pike and trout, but it sounds like you've got to be on time for your brother in Calgary."

"Yeah, we should keep moving. But it's been good swapping notes," I said.

"We were about to stop for dinner," Ben said. "Would you care to join us for a burger?"

"That's nice of you, but I'm meeting my girlfriend in about an hour and don't want to be late," he said, grinning. He was just shining up the newly installed headlight and closing the hood.

"Well, we certainly understand that. Don't want to make you late. Doesn't make a good impression," Ben said, smiling back.

I was ready to be generous when I asked, "How much do we owe you?"

His reply both caught me off guard and seemed perfectly natural at the same time. "You guys wouldn't have any smoke, would you?"

It was Ben's weed, so I looked at him. As friendly as we'd become with this guy in such a short time, a switch clicked in my head, signaling the crossing of yet another threshold, one with the potential for more than just a friendly encounter. Ben was a minor, I was 21 and for all intents and purposes his guardian on this trip, so the question had implications for both of us.

"I think we might just be able to help you out there," Ben said, sounding cautious in a friendly way. Immediately I was glad he said it. He followed with, "How much might a new headlight be worth?"

To which our mechanic replied, "Oh, not much. A joint, maybe two, depending on how you're fixed."

"I think we can manage at least that much," Ben replied and proceeded to roll three fat joints, at which the fellow beamed.

As we shook hands and exchanged thanks and goodbyes, he said, "I wish I was with you. I'd like to see more of the country. If you're ever back this way, be sure to stop in and I'll show you around. In the meantime, take care of yourselves. It's a long way to Dawson Creek."

Pulling out, Ben and I were quiet. I'm not sure what was on his mind. It could have been the realization that indeed it was a long way to Dawson Creek and that Dawson Creek was only the beginning of the Alaska–Canada Highway. Or it could simply have been an appreciation of a stranger's generosity. Both of these had crossed my mind. But what really struck me was the power of chance encounters to alter your life. How do you know when to trust the unknown? I was starting to note life dimensions I hadn't seen before and began to feel a little less wayward. I was hoping Ben did too.

Chapter 6

Over the next couple of days, we churned our way across Ontario, sleeping in the car on side roads and eating as we drove. We stopped about every 150 miles for gas as Route 117 scalloped its way, south and west, toward Thunder Bay. I was still doing the driving, Ben the rolling or map reading. But there really wasn't any navigation. Our road was always the biggest one headed west, though biggest isn't saying much. The Trans-Canada Highway is two lanes for its entire length, with the exception of a few divided highway sections through tourist areas in the Canadian Rockies.

We spent one night on the shore of Lake Nipigon, where, as we were setting up our tent Ben said, "I know Lake Nipigon." And then, turning to each other, together we recited, "Fourteen pounds, 5 ounces, 34½ inches long, the world record brook trout!" a fact we'd memorized from the *World Book Almanac*. It's easily seven times the weight of any brookie we'd ever caught.

I'd often drive past midnight, stopping only when the last cup of coffee had worn off. Without a radio, and with the steady droning of the V-8, Ben would get sleepy after a few hours of driving in the dark and crawl into the back seat and curl up. When I fully grasped the distances we were trying to cover, I drove later and later into the night. It was a comforting feeling, watching darkness overtake the world as the stars came out. I'd drift away, eyes glued to the beams of the headlights with only the company of the engine, the dashboard lights, and the occasional car passing in the opposite direction.

It began to dawn on me, as the odometer kept turning over, that what I was passing I would most likely never see again. I thought it was funny that sometimes thinking like that can leave you with a melancholic heart as it occurs to you just how little you will hold on to, while at other times, it can lighten your spirit as you surrender to the unique nature of every moment.

The evening we arrived in Thunder Bay, we parked and walked to the shore to watch the sunset over Lake Superior.

"Ben, you know we're only about thirty miles east of the eastern tip of Minnesota, but it feels like months since we've seen the states," I said. "According to this map, Isle Royal National Park is about twenty miles offshore, in that direction," I added, pointing southeast.

"I've read about the moose and wolf population studies they've done there," he said, looking at the map. "But the Michigan shore beyond it is still sixty miles farther."

"And over there," I said, pointing east, "is the Canadian version of Isle Royale, called Pukaskwa National Park. It's over a hundred and thirty miles across the water. And it's not even the widest point on the lake."

"Let me see that. Can't be," he said, taking the map.

The longest part, 350 miles, when multiplied by its widest, 160 miles, makes it the largest fresh water lake in the world by surface area.

"Holy smokes," Ben whispered. And then he paused, as if figuring something. After a moment he said, "Roughly, this lake is thirty–two thousand square miles. That's over three times the size of Vermont."

It was fitting that the Ojibwa named it Gichigami, meaning

"big water." Lake Superior could contain all the other Great Lakes and still have room for three more Lake Eries. Over 200 rivers feed it, entering from a shoreline 2,700 miles long. It's so deep that river water takes 191 years to exit. The ancient granites we were standing on, on its north shore, date from the Precambrian, four and a half billion years ago.

Up until now, I'd only thought of such vast scales with regard to mountains. After all, they loomed above you and hit you in your face with their enormity. Lake Superior changed all that. If there could be this much scale that I'd missed, what else had I failed to see so far? Was my understanding that superficial? That pitifully meager? It was one of those moments when you not only realize how little you know but also that your usual way of conceiving things has kept you from the wider sphere you seek.

I'd been on the road for only a few days and I was already reeling with the dimensions of the world. A journey without an itinerary can set you free to the point where you can become another random element in your own existence. You detach, separate from your "I–ness" and watch yourself with inert conductivity as you interact with the cascade of experiences you both create and encounter. Would I grow or crumble? Despite the optimism I'd felt earlier, at this point, I had no idea.

As the sun set over the lake, dark clouds rolled in from the west, and it started to rain.

"It seems a welcoming gesture on the lake's part, to give us thunder while we're standing in Thunder Bay," Ben said.

On the horizon, flashes of lightning opened the night sky. As we got back into the car, I was hoping that the electrical storm in my head was also illuminating the clouds in my mind.

Chapter 7

We entered the Central Time Zone just west of Thunder Bay. Time had changed now too, along with place.

Gas stations became our most frequent stops. There were two more before we hit the Manitoba border and said goodbye to Ontario and its water. Manitoba introduced us to the northern prairie and its heat. Having left the cool shade of the spruce forests behind, the temperature inside the car began to climb. We rolled all the windows down and began looking for a lake to swim in. We hadn't showered since leaving Vermont. But there were no more lakes, and the heat of the capital, Winnipeg, was inescapable. The highway ran straight as a gutter, without a curve for as far as we could see.

The map showed more of the same, with the whole lower third of the province covered with a grid of state highways, all running at right angles. Few roads traveled diagonally or had any curve in them.

Perhaps it was the monotony of the road or the endless flat horizon. Maybe it was the heat or the cumulative effect of the driving. But a few hours west, driving that night, I woke up with the headlights of the traffic now suddenly brighter in my eyes and realized I was in the oncoming lane. In panic, I overcorrected, swerved across my own lane, and hit the gravel shoulder, where the car spun sideways, coming to rest out of traffic with two suddenly very awake young men in it.

"You okay?" I asked the back seat.

"Yeah. I guess so. Jesus. What happened?" Ben replied, crawling up from the floor.

"I fell asleep at the wheel. Sorry, Ben. Really sorry."

"Maybe we should find a place to spend the night."

"Yeah. Let's do that."

And we did.

The following morning we crossed into Saskatchewan, although, except for the sign, we wouldn't have known it. The surrounding prairie looked the same, with wheat fields stretching off in all directions for as far as we could see. Grain elevators, some six stories tall, were the largest features on the horizon. We'd play a game, guessing how far off they were in miles and then watch the odometer. It was surprising how much we underestimated those distances. But if we guessed how long in minutes it would take us to reach them and then convert that time into miles at the rate we were traveling, we usually came out pretty close. Some of the elevators were over 20 miles from where we first spotted them.

“So how come, bro?” Ben asked.

“Well, here’s my take. We’re more accurate when we rely on our sense of motion, not just our vision. Maybe because motion gives you just that much more sensory input to go on. Plus, we’ve spent enough time in the car to gauge the rhythm of our progress relative to the terrain we’re crossing. It seems a human body in motion has its own sense of distance, which may or may not agree with its vision,” I replied.

“Well, thank you, Professor Peabody,” Ben said, smiling.

"Short version—if you keep moving, you get more clues."

"Pretty much," I replied. "It makes me think of Tim and me. Leaving home put us in motion. We got a bigger view outside the box we were all in. You stayed put, because you had no choice really, and observed from there. There's a payoff and a price with both."

"What do you think those were?" Ben asked.

"In leaving, we got immediate relief from the craziness at the house, but we put a distance between ourselves and you and Tamsen. And the place we escaped to was no paradise. You had to stay. There was probably less fighting with us gone, but you were left alone with Mom. It's not that one way was better than another. We were all just trying to deal with an insane home life, and in those cases there are no winners," I said.

"No," he replied. "Only survivors."

"Right."

That afternoon, we got pulled over by a Mountie, or rather, I should say, pointed over. He'd parked his cruiser on the shoulder with his flashing lights on and was standing next to it. With the road so flat, we could see him for a long way off, as could all the other drivers. We all slowed down, conscious of our speed, our attention drawn to his car and especially to him.

When he was sure you could see him, he raised his arm straight out and pointed his index finger at you and directed you to the side of the road up ahead, where another Mountie waited, to check your license and registration. This procedure left no doubt about what he wanted me to do.

Combined with his dead serious "Yes, I mean you" stare I immediately began to pull over. That's when I thought of Ben's reefer.

Both officers approached our car, as if having scored a real kill, and right away asked us to step out of it. One checked our papers and radioed them in while the other began searching the car: under the seats, in the glove compartment, even sniffing the rolled cigarette butts, which he must have thought were roaches.

Then he asked us to open the trunk of the car. But there he only turned a few items, continuing to ply us with questions about our trip, which we were more than happy to rattle on about. When his partner returned with our papers all checked and cleared, they told us we were free to go and to have a safe trip. And just like that they were on to the next target.

As I was getting into the Plymouth, the first officer raised his arm toward the highway and I could see the expression on the chosen driver freeze.

Down the road I asked Ben, "So, what'd you do with the pot?"

"I had it in my cargo pocket. I figured that would be the last place they'd look."

"Would you mind just throwing it out, Ben? That was just too close for me back there. It's not worth the risk. These guys are serious. And we don't exactly blend in. Two young long hairs with U.S. plates, from the land of the Woodstock Nation. Let's not make their job any easier. It isn't worth jail time."

"I don't want to do that, bro. Besides, at the rate I'm smoking it, it'll be gone soon. But if it'll make you feel any better, I'd be glad to smoke it all up by the side of the road right now." I knew there was more left than he or both of us could finish in one sitting, and it seemed a stupid thing to do, or about as stupid as keeping it on board. I didn't like the friction it made between us, and I didn't like feeling hostage to it either.

"No, that would seem like a waste. But do me a favor, will you? Be sure to keep it as well put away as you can."

"That's easy," he said. "I'll just keep it in my pocket."

It's only a little over 400 miles across Saskatchewan on Route 1, and we figured we could make it to Alberta the next day. If we just kept driving, we'd be that much closer to the airport where Tim was landing.

That's when I had the bright idea to ask Ben to drive.

Chapter 8

We were glad to leave Saskatchewan behind and enter Alberta, where we lost another hour to a time zone change and were back among places named for the surrounding land's features: Red Cliff, High River, Cold Lake, Red Deer. For the first time since Quebec, there were green blotches on the map, this time of two shades. The darker green of the provincial parks we'd seen before. But the lighter green of the Canadian national parks was new. And there was a lot of it.

Parklands ran for about 450 miles southeast to northwest along the border with British Columbia. The middle 250 miles contained four adjacent national parks: Banff, Kootenai, Yoho, and the largest and farthest north, Jasper National Park. The peaks in all of them averaged over 11,000 feet, with Mt. Robson, the highest at 12,972 feet, located in its own provincial park just east of Jasper. There were two other provincial parks flanking the spine of the Canadian Rockies on the west side. On the east side lay the Rocky Mountain Forest Reserve, over 250 miles long, which contained two wilderness areas, a recreation area over 100 miles long, and at least four provincial parks.

From Calgary we could see the snow on the peaks. In our rush, we'd arrived early, and had a week before Tim's arrival. But we didn't want to stay in the city when Banff, where we knew we could camp, was only about 75 miles farther. So we drove to Banff, where we spent the night in the car in a ski area parking lot, and woke to a whole new world.

Mountains rose all around us, and the snow they were draped with provided the source for the countless lakes, rivers, and streams we wanted to fish. Clouds lingered over the peaks and moved with the wind into the valleys. The overcast seemed a permanent part of the landscape. Falling streams and rushing water surrounded us. The spruce and hemlock forest was draped with moss, which also covered the forest floor and hung from arcing boughs. A myriad of greens formed the backdrop. It looked as though we'd just stepped into a living model of the hydrologic cycle. Water moved in all directions: rising in evaporation, falling in drops and currents, sweeping through branches. I didn't expect to see the sun any time soon.

And sure enough, it was the abundance of water that thwarted our first fishing trip. We decided to hike to a lake about nine miles up a creek and camp a few days. About three miles up, we came to a spot we had to ford. In crossing the waist-deep current, Ben lost his bedroll, a couple of blankets pinned together. It washed about 20 yards downstream before I could retrieve it, on the third attempt, a saturated mound. The stream was too high to cross; we were wet from the waist down and now hauled a drenched mountain of blankets that added another 20 pounds to our load. We decided to turn back, and then it started to rain, lightly at first, then settling in to an even, steady soaking.

At the trailhead, we must have looked pretty sad, because a friendly woman offered both of us a cup of tea, which we enjoyed in her camper. She told us about the spot that became our home for the next week, Eisenhower Campground, Banff

National Park, just up the highway. I was hoping Tim had brought plenty of clothes with him, as almost everything we had was soaked. With the high country still deep in snow, we decided to take day hikes to lakes in the vicinity. Welcome to the mountains.

The nearest laundromat was nearly 40 miles away in Banff, but it was time for dry clothes and groceries. When I stole the apple, peach and mixed nuts, I told myself it was all right as long as I paid for the other items I placed on the checkout. But two things happened I didn't see. First, Ben saw me do it and decided it was a game he wanted to play too. Second, the ratio of paid-to-lifted items changed, for the worse. But ignorance is only bliss until the consequences land.

That night, at Eisenhower Campground, I wasn't thinking about our escalating thievery. I welcomed our luck: the sun had finally come out as it was setting, most of what we owned was at least drier than it had been, and even though the campground charged two dollars a night, which I griped about, we were off the road and had found a home. From here, we could easily pick up Tim at the airport. On the way back from Banff, we'd actually even caught some trout.

And just as if it really were our home, our adjustment to it began to assume patterns. We'd wake up, usually to a mixture of rain and wind, and hike to a lake where it would rain some more. Once we got to a lake about four miles up the drainage and fished from shore without a strike. But there was a beautiful waterfall about two miles up the shore that held promise, so we started to bushwhack. It started to rain. Wondering if we should turn back, we stopped, and so did the rain. We'd continue and the rain would return. We finally decided to build a fire, and just as we'd gotten a steady blaze going, it started to pour. We hiked the four miles back in the rain. Standing near the Plymouth, I cast a lure into the outflow creek and caught a cutthroat trout that was all of four inches long.

"That's an inch of fish per mile hiked," Ben said, a rivulet running off his nose. "If that holds, we'll be doing some serious walking for keepers."

On our way back to camp, we'd stop at a store, where I'd shoplift a few items and pay for the others, Ben following suit. Then we'd warm up a can of Dinty Moore stew back at camp and sit by the fire, our boots and clothes spread all around. Ben and I played chess or he'd play his flute and I'd write. The rain had no trouble following a pattern either. It rained for six days straight.

On our way down from the lac du jour, Ben and I would sometimes plod in silence, while at other times, we'd have long conversations, often about family. It was during one such talk, squishing down the mountain in the rain, that we compared notes on our own family's connections.

Eight years of living apart had taken its toll. When Ben was enrolled at Northfield Mount Hermon, Mom went to Florida for a couple of months every year. Tamsen, two years older than me and away from home after college, was trying to get her life started, despite struggling with depression. Tim found the party, wherever it was, and worked in overdrive painting houses to support the spending that went with it. He and she hadn't spent more than an hour together in years. I was clinging to a routine that kept me busy and out of the house: an after-school and weekend job and drinking on the weekends with my few friends. I was closer to Ben in temperament than I was to Tim, whose speed seemed like it would soon overtake him. I liked a party well enough, but what I really wanted was to figure out where I was headed.

Right then I was headed down a trail that was quickly becoming a streambed and I turned around and said to Ben, "I'd like for us to at least try to stay together. We've spent eight years apart. I hardly know you or Tamsen. Tim has his own orbit. The families that only see their members at Christmas seem so distant and so lonely."

"I'm all for trying, but what if some members find the family expectations stifling?" Ben said.

"Then it's important for them and the family to at least accept one another's differences, and work toward understanding, right?" I replied. "That's an important skill for happiness in life. And the best place to learn it is in the family."

"What if someone feels that being himself only brings criticism?" he replied.

"All the more reason to work towards acceptance, not abandon it," I said.

"But what if the struggle for acceptance is too painful for them? That it's just more peaceful to detach," he replied.

"But how could it be peaceful without connection to his or her siblings or parents?" I asked. "Doesn't seem possible."

As it came out of my mouth, we both knew we were talking about ourselves. And that I thought I was the one trying, with Ben in the separatist camp.

"Being close doesn't always mean living together, or even close," I continued. "Being close is about sharing love and laughter when you're together. Accepting one another, even joyful for one another."

"True," Ben said. "And sometimes family members need to

be apart. It gives them the space and time they need to be themselves. Or to find their family of friends and their sense of identity."

"The thing is, we've been apart for so long that we haven't had much practice time," I said.

"That's for sure," Ben said.

I didn't know if we'd come any closer to healing, but at least now we were talking about it.

Chapter 9

The rain made firewood gathering a constant job, which we often enjoyed. Busting long branches warmed us, while the red squirrels scolded us for disturbing their peace. Small but bold, they provided great comedy. They'd steal crackers and even the peanut butter knife, and we'd roar with laughter that immobilized us until we chased them down. Even then, they were reluctant to surrender the knife. In my laughter, I was ignorant of the parallel in our own behavior.

There was plenty of downed wood for the fire near our campsite, all of it spruce, and once you got it going, it burned hot. The glow took the chill off, and our boots and jeans would start to steam as the day's rain rose to join the water cycle.

One evening we noticed that our elderly neighbor was struggling to get his firewood, so we brought him armloads and he thanked us warmly. It felt good to be a visitor helping a native, in the same way it did later, when we picked up the hitchhikers on our way back and helped them find a place to stay. Our small acts of kindness were always returned many fold, frequently by travelers, often by fellow campers. That night, after we returned from town, was an example.

The older gent we'd given wood to approached us to say that he'd held on to our campsite for us twice when families had begun to move into it in our absence. Grateful for his efforts, we made sure he had wood as long as he was camped there. Despite the misery that the days of clouds, rain and mosquitoes brought, this connection seemed to bring us together. In a way, I'd found a road family, the membership of which was open to anyone who was helping out. And for a while, it seemed as though every day brought new opportunities for someone to help us out.

We hiked to another high lake, and Ben grew an ugly blister on his foot from his new boots. He hobbled the last quarter mile to the lake, in the rain, with one bare foot. There was a family cozily ensconced on the shore with a tidy camp; they looked very dry to our dripping eyes. These people obviously had command of their situation. When they saw Ben's foot, they gave him a bandage, a small act of generosity, but one that left me feeling as though we couldn't take care of ourselves. The wind increased, and even though Ben and I are both decent fly fishers, we had trouble adjusting for the gusts and tangled our lines many times. When I hooked myself in the back of my head, I was ready for the therapist. And the weather, both outside and in, only got worse.

At camp the rain increased. Ben suffered with his blister, my scalp throbbed, and both of us were soaked and cold. We suffered in silence and said only what was necessary while fixing supper, buried in our misery. To relieve my frustration, I started splitting wood with our hatchet, but when a camper walked by with an axe, I saw a chance to really work off steam and asked if I could borrow it. Turns out, he'd borrowed it from another camper, so I brought the axe to the owner, the same man who'd saved our campsite for us, and asked if I could borrow it.

"Well, I don't know. I just got it. I suppose it'd be okay if you're careful with it."

I could sense his hesitancy and replied, "If it bothers you, I won't use it. I do have a hatchet."

He said, "No, I said you could take it." But perhaps feeling a need to help preserve his axe, he then rattled off a number of reminders about its use that only made me wish I'd never asked for it in the first place.

His seeming condescension aggravated my bad mood, which, though unrelated, heightened my friction with Ben. So I took the axe but returned it very politely about two minutes later, now even more riled. Ben and I were brooding in our silence when the axe owner walked up and started to chat. He told us about scenic hikes, places to climb, even a good place to get wood. As he was leaving he said, "I wasn't being huffy about my axe. It's just that I've gotten into the habit of not lending three things—my camera, my fishing rod, my axe—to anyone unless I know them."

I was floored. Placing his axe in the same company with two items I wouldn't lend to anyone made me realize just how trusting he'd been. I thanked him sincerely for his generosity and realized that once again someone we hardly knew had helped us. The Park Ranger even visited us that night, asked about our stay, and helped us with hiking tips, especially where the driest trails were likely to be. I felt that so many people had befriended me in one day that when the collecting agent dropped by, I gladly gave him the two dollars and knew we were getting a deal.

Chapter 10

The deal was even better than I had imagined when dawn broke the next morning. My anger had left with the night and the morning's clear sky and bright sun. Taking a tip from our axe–lending friend, Scov, we planned a hike from Morraine Lake up onto the slopes above it, in the Valley of the Ten Peaks.

With a 20–minute drive, we were hiking a switchback trail up a broad talus slope with the emerald lake shrinking the higher we got. At the first high meadow, we thought we'd reached the best view and lingered for a while before we realized even better, more dramatic ones lay waiting for us higher up. Another short hike brought us to a small alpine pond with a view of Sentinel Pass above it. It took us over an hour to hike less than a mile practically straight up over snow to the pass, but the view was full reward.

At over 8,000 feet, the pass affords a panorama of ten, 10,000 foot peaks curved in a giant horseshoe. We were standing in about the middle of the western arm of the horseshoe. The view to the rim on the eastern arm was surprisingly clear. I could detect single boulders, small snow patches lower down, larger snowfields higher up, meadow islands, and individual serrations in the ridge itself. The air space spanning this distance was so immense that it induced a sense of falling away into infinity. If you could spread your arms and glide to the valley floor, it would take you weeks to get down, or so it looked.

I was awed by the magnitude of scale, as in Thunder Bay. Here was my self/other profile drawn to full magnitude. My being was dwarfed by the immensity of the world. Here was my Lake Superior in the sky.

Hooting gleefully, we glissaded down the pitch in less than a minute. Even with our rear ends and boots soaked, the slide was so much fun that I didn't feel a great loss for having departed the view. Our first day of sun had provided a dimension of startling clarity, revealing both topographic and internal landscapes. But an unobstructed view of reality, even a very clear one, doesn't guarantee understanding. You must be looking for what is, not what you expect or want to see. This sort of assumptive misperception was being re-examined that same summer only a few mountain ridges over, in a shift that would revolutionize scientific thinking about the history of life on earth.

On the side of Mt. Wapta, 3,000 feet above the town of Field, a paleontologist, Harry Whittington, was conducting what was supposed to be a routine survey of a fossil bed called the Burgess Shale. An earlier scientist, Charles Walcott, had discovered it in 1909. At that time it had been recognized as the richest formation of fossils ever found, dating back 530 million years to the Cambrian explosion, the period in geologic time following the earliest known mass extinction.

A band of specimens only eight feet high and about 600 feet long, the Burgess Shale houses more anatomical diversity than all the world's seas today. It holds the only major soft-bodied fauna from the Cambrian era and provides our only window for viewing the beginning of life as we know it.

After collecting some 80,000 specimens over five seasons, Walcott classified them into the four existing major subclasses of arthropods, which is where they mistakenly lay for over fifty years. Of the 20 to 30 animal phyla now recognized, arthropods represent some 80 percent of all named animal species and, as such, represent the major path for tracking the history of life on earth.

Whittington, upon more careful examination of Walcott's specimens, began, very slowly at first, to revise their classification in a direction that grew to such radical proportions by the time he was finished, about ten years later, that the history of life on earth had been completely rewritten.

Whittington had established that, of the 22 different organisms found at the Burgess Shale, some 15 to 20 of them are so different from one another and so unlike anything now living that each ranks as a separate phylum. With this discovery, Whittington not only completely revised the history of life on earth but also forever after destroyed not just Walcott's classification but the shared assumption among paleontologists that life's history generally moves toward increasing complexity and diversity.

My view of the world from Sentinel Pass had been exceptionally clear, but how much of it was distorted by what I expected to see? And how much, or how little, was I expecting of myself?

Chapter 11

A few days later, Ben and I drove to Calgary to pick up Tim. We spotted his blond head floating above the crowd of arriving passengers. He looked up when he heard our shouts, his tan face smiling.

"So how was your flight?" I asked.

"No problems. I'm really glad to be here," he said. "This break sure is welcome," he added, drawing out the "sure" for emphasis. He grinned as he spoke and his blue eyes lit up.

"How was the job?" Ben asked.

"Bigger than I thought. Wore me out. We worked twelve-hour days the last week," he said.

"That's too bad," I replied, "but these mountains will give you a boost. We've got a great campsite, and found a spectacular hike we can do tomorrow."

"Cool. So how's the fishing up here? Got any monsters?" he asked.

Ben said, "We hiked to a few lakes and caught some trout. The streams are too high with rain to fish. Nothing big yet."

"Well, let's get to the lakes then," Tim said.

That night for dinner, we celebrated our reunion with our first restaurant meal of the trip and a large bottle of wine.

"I want to get into some big fish soon," Tim said, pouring his third glass. "Have you found a good lake?"

"Lake fishing has been disappointing, mostly because of the weather. Lots of rain and wind," I said. "Better weather should help, and there's no shortage of lakes to hike to."

Ben joined in. "We had a killer hike yesterday to a place called The Valley of the Ten Peaks. Really cool. Incredible views."

"The wildflowers are amazing—meadows full of intense colors in a sea of mountain grasses, surrounded by the remaining snowdrifts. In the sun, it's all glowing. And you're way up there, too," I added.

"Sounds spectacular," Tim said. "I sure am ready for some big fish, too. Those remote lakes should hold some."

We took Tim to Sentinel Pass the next day, anxious for him to feel the exhilaration of the altitude after weeks of painting houses. It was another perfect day, but like most descriptions you build up too much, or maybe because he just wanted to get to the fishing, the climb didn't excite him. He hiked out ahead of us to the summit and descended before us as well, in order to get some spin fishing in at Copper Lake, in the valley. But rushing prevented us from relaxing together, and the frenzied fishing was a bust.

Over the next few days we also escalated our filching whenever we picked up supplies. It occurred to me that with just Ben and me, the stealing had been a spontaneous affair, but with the arrival of Tim, it became an unspoken competition.

Before we left Banff on our way north the next day, we browsed the local tackle shop to ask about the best gear for the area. The sales people were helpful, freely offering suggestions about tackle and locations for where we were headed. As we were walking down the sidewalk, I was showing Ben the few lures I'd bought. When we turned the corner, Tim said, "Look what I got."

From the inside of his pants, he slowly pulled a brand-new spinning reel, still in its box. Ben and I chuckled nervously, then exclaimed, "Holy smokes, Tim!" We intended to show we were impressed with his deed, but I had a sickening feeling that our game had gone too far. I wasn't sure how to stop it.

As we headed north toward Jasper, the thieving became an overt competition, and we'd compare our booty after each stop for gas. It was small stuff: sugar packets, snack foods, or candy bars, and Ben took an active part as the little brother who could contribute his share. I watched him lift a few items though, and being new to this, he betrayed the necessary nonchalance with obvious jitters. When we entered the supermarket in Jasper and spread out, I was worried.

After cruising the aisles for what I thought we'd need, I checked out with the few items I'd dared to lift well hidden in my clothes. Then I walked outside and headed for our car. When I got what I thought was a safe distance from the store, I glanced back to see if anyone was following me. Spotting Ben, who was coming out of the store, I turned to approach him when he eagerly began, in a voice too loud, "Buck! You should see what I got!" He began to quicken his step and, without waiting to reach me, pulled a half pint of strawberries out of his pants. Then I noticed a man in a grocer's apron coming up quickly from behind him, and I tried to signal Ben. He was in the middle of his sentence, "I got–" when he was broken off by "You didn't pay for those, did you, boy? You need to come back in the store with me now."

I turned and walked, not daring to look back at Ben in fear of being caught myself. He needed someone not in trouble who could help him out. After leaving my groceries at the car, I walked back toward the store, looking for Tim. When we met on the sidewalk and I told him what had happened to Ben, he said, "Yeah, he was being too obvious, even telling me out loud what he was getting." We were walking in the direction we thought the police station was in when a cruiser pulled up.

The window rolled down and the officer asked, "You boys looking for your brother?"

When we responded, "Yes, officer," he replied, "Hop in. He's at the station."

The officer on duty said the clerk had caught Ben with over 30 dollars worth of groceries he hadn't paid for. When he read off every item, including a two-pound package of bacon, the sheer volume was impressive. Ben had been charged with petty larceny, and the case was scheduled to go before the judge at 1:30 the next afternoon. We were all expected to be there. When we were taken to his cell, he looked much younger than his fifteen years and certainly too young to be in jail. He still had his engineer's cap on, as if to project an air of nonchalance, but he grasped the cell bars with white knuckles and his pupils were dilated. I thought I saw sweat above his brows.

“How’re you doing?” I asked.

“I’m okay. A little nervous. What’d they tell you out front about springing me?”

“We just need to post your bond, which shouldn’t be any problem, and then you’ll be released. We just wanted to see you first,” I told him. “We’ve been scheduled to appear in court tomorrow afternoon.”

"How much is the bond?" he asked.

"I don't know yet, but it shouldn't be too much." I said. "I'm going out front to find out, and pay it. Then they'll release you. We'll either be in the front office or out on the sidewalk in front of this building. We're not leaving without you."

"I'll see you out front then," he said with a nervous smile.

"It'll only be a couple of minutes," I said as I squeezed his hand on the bar. Tim did the same and said, "See you soon."

The bail was twenty-five dollars and I paid it. Then we were instructed to wait outside for his release. A few moments later, Ben emerged from the back of the station, now beaming gleefully in his recovered freedom. As the oldest brother, I was worried about any trauma my little brother had experienced. I was about to launch into my best big-brother-as-counselor delivery when Ben pulled the cap from his head, revealing a two-pound bag of pistachios. Chuckling lightly, he said, "I sure am glad they didn't get these." We all roared with laughter. And relief.

With a shrinking afternoon in front of us, we didn't have enough time to find and set up a campsite and go fishing, so we did the next best thing, or so we thought. We found and booked a campsite, then went to check out the trout at the national hatchery in town.

There was the usual layout of long, narrow cement pools with different-sized fish in sections separated by dividers that let the current flow through from the head of the pool to the tail. We were impressed, Tim especially, with the size of the brood stock, and watched them intently. They were behemoth, easily running to five pounds or more and requiring larger cement pools to accommodate their two-foot plus length. They were healthy, too, and just cruising casually around the pool they'd occasionally throw in a burst of speed powerful enough to send off a sizable wake.

After returning to the site and setting up camp, we leisurely prepared a sumptuous meal complete with burgers and a green salad. We all seemed to be enjoying the relaxed pace; I know I was looking forward to a quiet evening around the fire after a stressful day. We were all munching cookies over tea when Tim quietly said, "I'd like to go back and snag some of those big breeders."

I thought he was joking. "Yeah, right. It's only the national hatchery, and we've only got to be in court tomorrow to face the judge," I said.

"No, I'm not kidding," he continued. "We could park off a parallel road and come in through the fields. The fence is only eight or nine feet. It would be easy to get over it. I'd love to get some of those fish." At that point, I looked at Ben, who was gaping in Tim's direction.

Trying to sound supportive, but at the same time letting my disagreement be known, I said, "Well, yeah, sure, it would be nice to get some of those fish, but we don't know what's going to happen with Ben tomorrow, and if we get caught, the judge is going to be very annoyed, and rightly so. Ben, and all of us for that matter, could take a huge hit."

"Look, it's a warm night and with the half moon we've got there'll be plenty of light. Besides, when are we going to get back here again? Probably never." And then he added, "I'm going." End of discussion.

We sat in icy silence. So what were we to do? Let him go alone? Without an accomplice to act as lookout or to help him scale the fence with a large struggling fish, if he got that far, his chances of getting caught increased. If that happened, we'd worsen our fate for sure. I also knew that my stature as big brother would collapse if I didn't go along. I'm sure he also realized his chances for success improved with my help. He was ready to take the risk and was double–daring me to join him. I'd be a coward if I didn't.

Chapter 12

That's how we ended up parked in a tall–grass meadow off a parallel road from the hatchery under a half moon, with dark clouds drifting in front of it. It was humid and looked like it might rain. Ben, already at risk, stayed with the car, while Tim and I approached the hatchery through a small stand of trees and into a field spotted with clumps of bushes. Just before the fence, I noticed Tim was wearing gray corduroys and suggested he change to my brown ones to help avoid being spotted. After we exchanged pants, Tim was over the top of the fence quickly and at the edge of the pool.

I could hear the fish thrashing as he struggled to corral them with his too small net, and kept my eye trained on the cabin, not far away, where I could see the warden sweeping the floor. It sounded like Tim was about to win the struggle, and, expecting he'd need help, I shifted my view toward him. Out of nowhere, an incredible boom of thunder shook the atmosphere, and, looking back to check the warden's reaction, I was surprised with the view of a single, dangling light bulb but no warden.

In an effort to locate him, I then peered even more intently into the darkness surrounding Tim, and my heart stopped. Crouched six feet behind Tim, who was too busy with the fish to notice, was the warden, about to strike.

"TIM! RUN!" I screamed. The warden lunged. Tim ducked and then bolted for the fence. His adrenaline–fueled first leap onto the fence landed him more than halfway up it, hands grabbing the top edge, with only two steps to clear it. That was when the warden latched onto his lower leg and wouldn't let go. There was a brief, intense struggle before Tim shook him off and swung over, hitting the ground sprinting.

"We'd better split up. I'll meet you back at the car," he said between his gasps as we raced across the field.

I watched him peel off toward the river. I ran until my lungs were about to burst and stooped over, heaving for air. I would have been content to walk from there, but I looked back toward the hatchery, where three cruisers, flying over the rise, were speeding toward the warden's cabin. They arrived so fast I was able to see them get out, their powerful flashlights sweeping the field. And then I heard their dogs. "God, please help Tim," I thought. "If we get out of this, I promise never to do anything bad again." Muttered like a true jerk. And then I started sprinting.

As if to confirm my self–assessment, the sky opened up and it began to rain hard. Even though I was totally soaked, the pelting rain was a relief. Alhough it reduced my visibility and sense of direction, at the same time it shrouded my movement and blurred my tracks. I was grateful it would be doing the same for Tim.

When I arrived at the spot where I thought we'd left the car, it wasn't there. I looked around carefully and realized I wasn't in the right place. I oriented myself to where I thought the paved road should be, and set off again, weaving my way to another spot that I thought looked familiar. But no.

I tried again and again, but each time I found a clearing I was sure would have the car sitting in it, it was empty, with no tracks through the grass or any other signs. I wasn't even sure anymore where the paved road ought to be.

I'd been searching for over an hour. The rain was steady, and besides being soaked, when I was forced to walk through thickets, I started getting cold. I worried about Ben, who would be worried himself as the night moved toward dawn, with the white Plymouth then exposed in the daylight. The later we returned, the more we increased his worry and his vulnerability.

I retraced my steps through all my diversions but couldn't find my way back to the original terrain from which I'd run. Having gone in all the directions I thought were right, I tried those that remained.

On the first foray, I didn't see anything that looked familiar. Ditto on the second. On the third try, at the distance I thought I should turn around, I spotted a clump of trees that gave me promise and walked toward them, and then through them. On the far edge of the trees I spotted the car, sitting right in the open in the field where we'd left it, with Ben on guard duty. I could even make out the glow from the anxious drags on his cigarette. One look at his face told me how thoughtless we'd been to leave him alone. His quivering lips left no doubt.

"Am I sure glad to see you," he said with relief. "I was really worried that something had happened. Where's Tim?"

"I don't know. He's still out there. I'm sorry, Ben," I began. "This was a stupid idea. A really stupid idea. We split up. The warden spotted Tim and nearly nabbed him. He ran for the river and I came this way. It's taken me nearly two hours to find my way back. For a while there, I didn't think I would. I looked back to see if I could see Tim just before I had my last glimpse of the hatchery. Three cruisers were pulling in, and the cops were getting out with search dogs. I sure hope he's okay."

Ben took another nervous drag on his cigarette. "Search dogs, really? That's bad," he said.

"The rain will dilute Tim's scent," I said, trying to relieve Ben's worry. "But even without the scent, the dogs can catch Tim if they see him. And the sun will be rising pretty soon. It's after three now. In less than two hours, this car is going to stand out in this clearing. But we've got to wait as long as we can."

There wasn't anything to do except wait, worry, and hope, in the longest, darkest silence I'd ever remembered. Dire outcomes plagued my brain. We were due in court in less than 12 hours.

The rain pounded the car as we stared through fogged windows toward the direction we hoped Tim would return from. But our vision was as obscured and murky as our thoughts, and the longer we waited the greater the tension wore on us. We smoked cigarette after cigarette, watching the sky lightening in the east. Then suddenly, brush rustled nearby. I panicked briefly, then breathed as the rear door opened and Tim scrambled in.

"Are we ever glad to see you!" Ben and I both exclaimed at the same time, extending high fives. "What happened?"

Then we noticed that he'd been swimming and was covered in leaves and twigs. He looked like a Special Forces commando who'd just returned from a covert night mission. Water dripped from him everywhere. His hands were white. His forehead was scratched and bleeding. He was panting.

"The river saved me," he said softly, shivering. "At one point there was a guy with a flashlight and a dog about twenty feet from where I was hiding, but I managed to slip into the current and escape. I had to run a couple sets of rapids. I was a long way from the car before I thought it was safe enough to get out of the water, but here I am. Let's fire up the heater. I'm freezing."

I started the Plymouth and, without lights, we crept through the field and back onto the road. Even though it poured all night, we slept, as Huck Finn would say, like dead people.

When we entered the court that afternoon, I felt that we'd been offered a reprieve from our barely averted disaster the night before. I was ready to take what the court would give and consider ourselves lucky. Ben scanned the full courtroom and tensed. Tim looked undisturbed. We'd been scheduled for the afternoon session and were required to appear at its beginning, 1:00 p.m., although we didn't know when we'd be called. Looking around, it didn't seem like anyone else did either. We quietly took seats in the gallery.

The judge entered and the clerk called, "All rise. Honorable Judge so–and–so now presiding over Her Majesty's court, Jasper, Alberta, July 20, 1972. God save the Queen." The courtroom responded with a firm repetition, "God save the Queen," and then we all sat down.

As we watched, the resolution of the cases before us rattled my sense of relief. One defendant was sentenced to three months in jail for possession of marijuana. The next was sentenced to a month in jail for robbing a cigarette machine. All of a sudden, the prospect that we could be staying in Jasper for longer than we wanted started to seem quite real.

The afternoon seemed eternal, and combined with the wait

in the dark the night before, I was beginning to feel that we'd created our own purgatory on this trip and were carrying it with us. After three hours, the courtroom was emptying and it looked as though we wouldn't be called. Then the clerk announced our case, and we were instructed to approach the bench. I walked to the front with Ben. The judge, appraising us, seemed ready to go home himself. "How do you plead?" he said plainly.

"Guilty, Your Honor," Ben replied.

"The court orders you to pay a fine of ten dollars. You may see the court treasurer for this. Case dismissed."

"Thank you, Your Honor," I replied. Ben and I turned toward the foyer, where we would pay the fine, and glanced at each other. The mutual relief beamed across our faces. Purgatory had lifted.

Chapter 13

From Jasper to Dawson Creek, which is the beginning of the Alaska–Canada Highway, it's nearly 600 miles. By the time we left the courtroom it was late afternoon. We got gas, parked, and fixed a quick dinner of beans, bread and tea. Glad to leave our past behind, Tim and I took turns at the wheel, stopping for coffee when needed, and drove all night. We said little—partly from fatigue, partly from relief, and maybe even partly because we knew we had caused our own trouble and were lucky to have escaped unscathed. It was a pensive night's driving.

Having gassed up just south of Dawson Creek, we had no reason to stop there, so we kept traveling north to the town of Fort St. John, about 40 miles farther, where the pavement ends. The change to gravel is the point at which drivers have to armor their vehicles.

Like a gallant knight preparing his mount for a medieval joust, AlCan drivers must cover the headlights and install protective screens on their cars. The screens are mounted on the front bumper, extend up higher than the hood of the car, and guard the grillwork and radiator from damage while also providing enough lift to throw the stones over the windshield. The headlights get their own clear plastic domes as an additional layer behind the screens. All of this you install yourself.

Without having slept, we stumbled into an auto parts store in Fort St. John and realized we should have done our shopping in Dawson Creek, where there would have been more competition and lower prices. Being new to this, we chose a basic setup that, while not offering the most security, looked as though it would be adequate. We were floored when the man behind the counter told us the price. We were more than floored; we were angered at what we saw as an obvious attempt to gouge us. In our self-centered naiveté, we were convinced the seller was deliberately overcharging us because he didn't like the way we looked. It was either pay the man or suffer the time and expense of an 80 mile round trip to Dawson Creek. Seething, we paid up and left, throwing our purchase in the trunk.

And then something strange happened, as if to confirm our outrage.

A guy about our age, bicycling by on the road, looked at us and said in a disgusted tone, "Why don't you fairies get haircuts? You look like a bunch of girls."

The insult on top of the perceived price gouging was too much for Tim to bear. While Ben and I stood flat-footed in disbelief, Tim dropped his packages and bolted after the rider. Within a few steps Tim realized he had no chance of catching him and raced back to the car and hopped in. We jumped in too, grabbing his dropped load when we realized we'd be left behind, and Tim floored it. The biker looked back when he heard us roaring up behind him and stood up on the pedals in a mad dash to escape. He shot quickly down an alley and Tim followed at reckless speed, the Plymouth leaning sharply.

The contents of the dashboard slid, crashing to the floor,

and the cargo in the trunk rolled in a wave that collided with the spare tire. The rider had a lead, but the alley, though narrow, was straight, and Tim floored it again. In the blur, we creased a couple of garbage cans and skimmed a dumpster. The rider was pumping furiously, trapped by the psycho closing fast. Tim put the Plymouth's bumper within a foot of the bike's rear tire and started smiling.

"Call me a girl, will ya?" he muttered. The rider glanced back with a look of terror. I clutched the dashboard and Ben the back of the rear seat, bracing for contact. And then, lifting his foot from the gas pedal, Tim let the car drift back as the end of the alley approached, where it emptied onto a main street. The rider, still escaping, braked abruptly and skittered the bike into a left turn. Tim turned right, gently blending into traffic and said, "I think I made my point."

The pavement ended, the gravel began, and within minutes we had all the proof we needed that the protective shielding was a wise, if costly, purchase. It was still over 800 miles to Whitehorse, half the distance to Fairbanks, and cars coming from that direction looked beaten. Some had cracks running the length of the windshield, shattered headlights, and mud all over the body, sometimes so thick we couldn't tell what color the car was. The traffic was sparse, so every specimen offered a long view.

Mostly loose gravel, sometimes packed, the road only permitted speeds between 30 and 40 miles per hour. Faster than that you endangered the car's suspension and your nervous system. The endless miles of washboard, potholes, and rocks careening off the car's undercarriage served as a firm governor of your speed. The vibrations rattled the glass in the doors, threatened the exhaust system, and shook wiring loose. When it rained, which it did often in this temperate rainforest, the road became a quagmire, with rolling whalebacks of jellied earth ready to swallow you up to your axles. When the road was dry, you choked on dust. Over concern that we'd succumb to one of these hazards if we stopped for longer than necessary, we kept rolling.

The road was laid out during World War II by engineers who were in a hurry to open an overland route to Alaska, which the Allies thought might be a point of attack by the Japanese. In this rainforest, drainages were numerous and streambanks provided the line of least resistance to the bulldozers. But they were wet, and the Army Corps of Engineers lost a few D9s in the morass.

Following watercourses perpetuated the road's swampy condition, and, lined on both sides by significant ranges, there were few, if any, points where a traveler could get a view more distant than the nearest looming summit. You were traveling along the bottom of a very high-walled trough, where all the weather's excesses collected. We saw thick spruce and fir forest, low cloud cover, constant rain, and the road in front of us. Our slow speed kept even steady progress to a minimum, so with this misery as impetus, we drove all day and night for two days. When we pulled into Laird Hot Springs, at four in the morning, we were desperately ready for a long soak.

To get to the hot springs we hiked over an elevated boardwalk that crossed a swamp. The swamp flowed with the warm runoff from the springs, creating a mist that rose in the early morning light. It was peaceful and eerie at the same time, with the boardwalk vanishing into the distance. In the fog, we had no reference point ahead of us or behind, only the boardwalk underneath. We followed this walkway into the mist for what seemed like a long time.

Expecting to see the hot springs soon, we kept our eyes on the furthest point we could see in front of us and were halted by the sight of a large cow moose and her two calves standing in the swamp, about to cross the boardwalk. The calves stepped clumsily up onto it, lurching to keep their balance while trying to avoid the gaps between the planks. They were comical in their gawkiness, and their staggering gave us the first smiles we'd had in a while. First, one stumbled up, across and down, then the other, as we watched with amusement. When she was sure both of her calves were safely across, the cow took her turn, and with one gargantuan stride, like a giant construction crane walking in slow motion, she cleared the boardwalk, first with each of her front legs, then with each of her rear ones. We watched as the trio disappeared into the mist.

We approached the spot where they had crossed, astounded at the sight of the cow's tracks on either side of the boardwalk.

"You believe the size of that cow?" I asked.

"Had to have been at least six feet at the shoulder," Tim replied.

"What do they hunt these moose with? A cannon?" Ben quipped.

The boardwalk led us a long way farther, but the sight of the actual hot springs explained why someone had gone to the bother of building it. Unlike other natural hot springs, these were big enough to allow swimming, not just bathing. They were over-your-head deep and wrapped with smooth rocks, permitting easy entry and exit. And the odor of sulphur, though strong, was not unbearable. Our immersion was complete, both physically and mentally, and we had the place to ourselves. We left relaxed an hour later and shuffled back down the long boardwalk to the campground.

That evening it looked as though it might rain and we were too tired to set up a tent, so we shot it out for who'd get to sleep in the car. Ben and I won. Tim dragged his bag off into the bush nearby and we were all comatose within minutes. At some point, I was shocked into the conscious world with Tim banging on my window, shouting, “Let me in! Let me in! There's a grizzly out here!” I lunged for the door, jerked the handle and pushed, and he dove through the crack onto me and then onto the floor.

"That was close," he gasped. "A grizzly stumbled over me, then backed up and snorted. Then it sat up and sniffed. It smelled horrible. I froze in my bag. Then it leaned back down on all fours and walked away. It's still around here. Make sure we lock the doors."

We all turned, locking the nearest doors. When his gasping subsided, I asked him, "Are you all right?"

"Yeah. It just scared the hell out of me. I didn't know if it was going to attack me and there was nothing I could do."

" Must have been hard to stay still," Ben said.

"I was frozen," Tim said. “That’s the closest I want to be to a grizzly, or any bear for that matter. Let’s be sure to all sleep in the car in territory like this. If I’d come between a sow and her cubs, it could have been lights out.”

“No kidding,” I said. “We’re in bear country now and let’s not forget it. That was a warning. Let’s get a little sleep and check for tracks later.”

"Sounds good to me," Tim said. The color had returned to his face and his breathing was normal.

Then he and I made ourselves as comfortable as we could together in the back seat of the Plymouth and, after deep snoring followed the rhythm of regular breathing, I finally dropped off.

The sun woke us all, and we gradually oozed out of the shelter of the car and drowsily began to clean up the landfill in the Plymouth. The big trunk lid was raised, all the doors were open and we were silently shuffling around in circles, sorting gear and culling debris, when I spotted some movement in the clearing at the hot springs trailhead.

Profiled clearly in the morning sun, four grizzlies calmly walked through the dirt parking area, like a line of elephants entering the center ring.

"Nobody move," I said quietly.

Ben and Tim looked my way and I nodded toward the bears. The two in the lead were large and the two trailing were younger and smaller. Perhaps 40 feet off, they looked casually from side to side, their heads bobbing as their massive shoulders rippled. Maybe they didn't see us. If they smelled us, they made no sign. A morning stroll? Headed for the river for some breakfast salmon?

Within moments they'd disappeared into the forest, and we all smiled. "Did we just see four grizzlies?" someone asked.

"Sure did," someone else said. "Those beasts were massive."

"Wonder if one of those big ones was the one Tim met last night," I said.

"It was too dark to get a good look. And I wasn't focused on what the bear looked like," Tim answered.

Ben said, "Makes me wonder just how many bears there are around here. We should be careful moving through the brush."

"They could be moving to the river, and we're in their path," Tim said.

"We should give them time to move out of the area," I said.

"Maybe we should move out of their area," Ben said. "But not until after we've had a good breakfast. Not instant oatmeal and raisins and brown sugar."

"Eggs, maybe." Tim said.

"And big slabs of bread, smeared with jelly," Ben added.

"And tea," I said. "Lots of tea."

Chapter 14

After breakfast, the driving took over. Sixty hours of it, mostly nonstop, over the road to our adventure, the road itself becoming the adventure. In some places, the top two inches of surface were a stew of stones, sand, silt, and clay, which flowed glacially toward the low side of the road and in turn, was replaced by the slurry sliding down slope from above. There were points where the surface was smoothed by this slow current long enough that, at the wheel, you could feel the road skin sliding under the tires. You had to counter not just the bends and rises, but the conveyor belt of sludge pulling you off-road, toward axle-eating muck waiting patiently for you to make a mistake. It was my turn first.

After a stretch of driving equal to about three peanut butter sandwiches, made for me and passed forward by whatever brother was in the back seat, an ominous grinding began from somewhere in the rear of the car. I ignored it at first, thinking it was a lodged stone or stick that would eventually fall out. When I pulled over, I shouldn't have.

When I leaned on the car to inspect the underside, it started settling and then, alarmingly, started sliding downhill as I watched the tire disappear, with the rim about to follow. My two brothers were out of the car in a shot.

"Quick! Start it up! We need to push it NOW!" Tim yelled.

Ben leapt behind the wheel. Tim and I heaved, the bumper plenty low now for leverage. Footing fell away from us as we watched first our shoes, then our socks, get covered with ooze, still without any forward movement.

"Gun it, Ben!" Tim yelled, and the spinning tires, now turbines, launched a quilt of mud. Lifting and dropping the bumper in unison, we were heartened as the tires slowly gained bits of purchase and the car began to move toward the center of the road. Tim and I groaned with exertion, and one final tremendous heave nudged the car into the center of the road, idling. Tim and I bent over double, gasping.

Mud was suddenly the compelling new fashion statement. Mud dripped from mid–shins, mud covered the entire rear of the car, and mud plastered our pants and sweatshirts. Ben got out of the car and waited while we caught our breath.

"That was close. Hey, I haven't seen this much mud since preschool," Tim huffed.

"What do you say we get this crate moving before it joins the Titanic?" Ben shot back, and we all fell into our reclaimed flagship, smearing mud all over the inside. Underway, the first thing I noticed was that the scraping noise was gone.

Whitehorse was the next major stop, famous for the hardships of the miners trying to scale the Chilkoot Pass to the gold fields of the Yukon in the 1890s. Robert Service had made their struggles famous with his collection of poems, *The Spell of the Yukon and Other Verses* in 1907. Only now, we were the "cheechakos," the newcomers to the goldfields he described. His poems, which I'd read along with Hermann Hesse and Thoreau, described the beauty of the wilderness and the strength it took to survive there. Their rhyme was driven headlong in couplets packed with intensity, continually reminding me of life's ticking clock:

> There's the wretched rent to pay,
> Yet I glower at pen and ink;
> Oh, inspire me, Muse, I pray,
> It is later than you think!

As an ambulance driver during World War I, Service had written *The Rhymes of a Red Cross Man*. The poems became the source for Country Joe McDonald's anti-war rock album in 1971, and the author, through Country Joe and the Fish's hit song, "I Feel Like I'm Fixing to Die Rag," joined the voices opposing the Vietnam War.

It was still raining and dreary when we arrived in Whitehorse, and the swollen Yukon River carried all that the rain had washed into it. The watershed of the Yukon River above Whitehorse is roughly 10,000 square miles, so there is a lot of debris. Whole trees, rolled by standing waves five feet high, slammed the bridge abutments, creaked and snapped, and were then shot downstream. The roar of the churning, swirling maelstrom, chocolate with sediment, drowned our voices as we watched from the gas station. The raging torrent gnawed the banks, calving car-sized chunks of earth into the current.

We weren't thinking fish. Not possible. We weren't even thinking boats. We were thinking survival. If you fell in, there'd be no way you could be rescued. Even given its tremendous power and size at this point, the Yukon River was still over 1,5000 miles from joining the Bering Sea.

The city gets its name from the White Horse Rapids, said to

look like the mane of a white horse, but these weren't them. White Horse Rapids had been drowned under a lake formed by the construction of a hydroelectric dam in 1958. The city had sacrificed its namesake and its wild river to quench its thirst for electricity, in the mistaken belief that doing so would bring wealth and progress.

This pattern has been repeated over and over again throughout the world's river systems, with one of the worst examples only a few hundred miles south in the U.S.

The Grand Coulee and its fellow 14 dams on the Columbia River main stem have destroyed one of the world's largest and most valuable salmon fisheries. In 1995, the International Commission on Large Dams funded a study of the Columbia River dams, which concluded that the lost salmon would have been worth more than the electricity generated by all of the over 200 hydroelectric dams in the entire river basin. Yet without their consent, the generations that have followed, both white and First Nation, were deprived of their free rivers, their salmon, and the wealth of a healthy environment.

We were halfway to Fairbanks.

Change from the gas purchase included a Canadian five-dollar bill, which had an engraving of impressive waterfalls on the back.

"Otter Falls aren't far from here, you know," the attendant said when he saw me examining the print. "A left off the AlCan about forty miles north. It's about eighteen miles in on a one-lane road, but it's worth it. Especially if you're looking for some fishing."

The turn was right where the attendant said it would be, and the road was certainly one lane: no shoulder, no pull offs.

And the falls were definitely worth it.

As wide as they were tall, and flowing through a tangled snarl of tree trunks and cliff faces, the water gushed in all directions. The falls, perhaps 30 feet high, held huge fences of interwoven debris, behind which water pooled and swam back on itself before bursting from a leaky seam or surging over a lip. While we watched, sections of jam would let go and plummet with a snapping crash or would suddenly shift, hurtling walls of water over edges. More trunks from the lake above would funnel toward the drop and curl over, sometimes bouncing end over end until they jammed. With all of this oxygen and the channeled flow of nutrients leaving the lake, there had to be trout here, and we caught them right away—brilliant rainbows, which steamed right for the nearest snag when hooked.

The rain suddenly seemed less oppressive, a feeling enhanced when a friendly old couple invited us to their camper for soup and surprised us with a side order of lake trout they'd caught in Otter Lake. We must have looked pretty ragged to them, and we were careful not to shake too much mud onto the floor of their camper. We swapped information about the AlCan and where we were headed and, as a final gift, they showed us to a shelter on the lake with a stove. The walls came up only three feet from the floor, which was woodchip-covered earth, but the roof was tight and it looked like a palace to us. There was plenty of firewood lying around, and the stove's warmth was a welcome relief from the constant rain. With a dry floor of chips to sleep on, it was downright cozy.

The Plymouth's exhaust had developed a roar too loud to bear. Our patch on the exhaust wasn't working, so Tim and I decided to take the car to Johnson's Crossing, and Ben said he'd stay at camp and keep the fire burning. Johnson's Crossing, the nearest point for repair, was back down the Otter Creek Falls Road to the AlCan and about 20 miles north. Only 38 miles, one way. From its dot on the map, we knew it would be small. Just how small surprised even us.

Standing in a small clearing bulldozed from dense spruce was a newsstand-sized plywood building with a single door and a lone, hand-operated gas pump out front. When we pulled in, a thickly bearded, wild-haired man wearing a worn jumpsuit, who looked to be in his thirties, walked out to greet us.

"Can I help you?" he said, smiling.

"We'd like to get our exhaust repaired," I said.

"Yeah, I heard it as you pulled in. Why don't you pull the car away from the pump a bit and I'll get under there and see what I can do."

As we pulled it over, he returned to the newsstand and came out tugging a floor jack across the gravel. He jacked up the rear of the Plymouth, placed jack stands under each side of the axle and went back to the newsstand, this time emerging with an acetylene torch on a hand truck.

"I've got no parts to splint the broken exhaust pipe with, but I can weld it and hopefully it will hold up for you," he said, rain dripping off his face.

And then, lying in the bare gravel under the raised car, he did just that. It took him a while because, as he explained, he had to keep the torch's flame away from the gas tank, a procedure that required many trips back and forth in the rain to the shed for shielding material. He worked for more than two hours, and when he was finished he put away all his equipment, let the car down, and dragged the jack back to the shed.

We'd been standing under the eave, trying unsuccessfully to stay dry. When he came out, his jumpsuit was smeared with mud, heaviest on his shoulder and hips. His knees and elbows showed through ragged holes. His hands were blackened, fingernails jammed with grease. The rain running off his hair fell onto his face, where it washed little rivulets through islands of sand and mud. He was still smiling.

"That should hold for a while, but I can't make any guarantees," he said.

I wanted to acknowledge how hard he'd just worked and show our thanks, but after our purchase of the rock shield in Fort St. John I was worried that he was going to charge heavily for his labor.

"Seemed like a tough job in difficult conditions," I managed.

"No more so than usual. It rains a lot here and my resources are thin," he replied.

"Well, we appreciate your help," I said. "How much do we owe you?"

"How does twelve dollars sound?"

Sounds generous to me," I said, handing him the bills. "And the exhaust is music to our ears."

"Good luck, guys. It's a long road."

"Thanks, again," Tim said.

As we pulled out, I realized we hadn't even bought any gas.

The newly recovered quiet inside the car was a treat, and Tim and I could enjoy conversing without having to shout. It was still raining just as hard and the temperature was dropping, but the steady churn of the V–8 and the wonderful blast from the heater brought security and confidence.

"Now this sure is nice," I said.

"No kidding," Tim replied. "I can hear you."

I was checking the map. "Hey, it's only two hundred and twenty miles to the Alaska border, where the road turns to pavement, and only five hundred to Fairbanks. We're closing in."

"I hope we can afford to fly into the arctic from there. That would be amazing fishing," he said.

"Can you imagine—five pound arctic char?" I asked.

"And eight-pound rainbows?" Tim added.

We were sharing these dreams when we spotted in a meadow four shapes that we knew weren't dogs. But they were too big to be coyotes, either.

The sight was so startling that Tim stopped the car in the middle of the road and shut off the engine. Wolves. They were loping, trotting with their heads down mostly, attention elsewhere. Branching off, circling back, following lines of scent maybe, they were casual, and seemed to be out on a cruise through the neighborhood, reconnoitering. One was dark, almost black, but the one in the lead was gray, and the others seemed to be following him. They were relaxed, at home, and carried themselves with comfortable expectation of what that home would provide. They seemed to know that it had already provided and that their work now was to find those provisions. We gazed as they drifted back into the forest, a piece of the wild blending into itself.

"That's really cool. Wolves in the wild," Tim said.

We drove on in silence a few miles down the road, when a tire threw a stone under the car, where it hit the welded exhaust and opened it again.

"That stone just broke the weld," Tim said. "Great."

"The quiet sure was nice while it lasted. Glad it gave us the chance to see the wolves," I said.

"That's true. Maybe we can get a better fix in Fairbanks," Tim replied, as we droned our way back to the falls.

When we pulled into the shelter, the first thing Ben said was, "I thought you were going to get the exhaust fixed."

"Can't you hear how quiet it is now?" I said, smiling. The true story was some consolation. He lit up with our report of wolves.

"How big were they? How many of them were there? What were they doing? Did they see you?"

Around the warm stove and a hot bowl of canned beef stew, our description of the pack slipped the still-broken exhaust and the cold, hard rain into the background.

We'd fished all we wanted at the falls, so the next day, despite the protection and roomy warmth of the lean-to from the ceaseless rain, we packed the car and drove out to the AlCan and about 30 miles north, passing the newsstand garage to a small river we'd heard about from the anglers at the falls. The road into it was another single track, which we followed for a few miles until it crossed the river. A Japanese pickup truck with Ontario plates and a small camper on it was parked in the meadow just off the road and we pulled in next to it. We didn't see anyone around to ask about the fishing, so we just started casting lures and were immediately into fish. They were grayling, fish we'd never caught before, and, as one of a few species found only above the Canadian border, they delighted us and confirmed our arrival in the far north.

Fish were the creatures we were most interested in, and here was one so exotic it dwelled in our awareness as myth. Grayling had the appearance to match their reputation. They were shining silver and purple cylinders with a soft, downward-facing mouth. But despite their opalescent shimmer, their riveting feature was their dorsal fin, growing from their back like a rippling rhombus, out of all proportion to their size—the sailfish of the riparian world. A large one was a foot long, with most around ten inches, and although we caught them one after another, we never ceased to marvel at the fantasy they presented. It was like landing unicorns.

At one point, Tim felt a movement and looked down to see two black, beady eyes in a burrow between his feet. On the next cast, he caught a grayling and dangled it down the opening. In a flash, the critter ripped it from his hand and vanished.

"You think you're so smart, eh?" Tim chuckled.

The next cast brought another grayling and Tim said, "You're not getting this one," as he lowered it into the hole. With a flash, it was gone.

"Better watch your fingers," Ben warned. "That guy is fast."

With the third fish, Tim wove his finger through the grayling's gills and lowered it once more into the burrow. We heard a snarling snap as the mink took the bait and the tug-of-war was on. Tim managed to pull the grayling out a few inches, and the mink would reset his teeth into new flesh and yank himself back down the hole.

"You met your match now, Tim. He's not backing down," I said, laughing.

"Watch this. I'm going to drive him crazy," Tim replied. We were all laughing with each new lunge.

Tim kept backing up, trying to keep all his fingers. He was also smiling from ear to ear.

Then another pair of eyes appeared in the burrow, and the

whole affair became a circus act, with Tim as ringmaster keeping his balance between a pair of lunging mink.

"Better watch out now, Tim. They're double teaming you," Ben shouted between laughs. Neither he nor I made a move to help him.

With two sets of teeth to dodge, Tim was moving much quicker, and backing up, with the mink following him further and further out of their den. But with their increasing distance from safety, they were becoming more and more nervous and they kept glancing back. The mink were shrieking and snarling even louder, and with Tim's chuckles and cajoling and our laughter on the sidelines, we were raising quite a commotion.

The owner of the pickup truck emerged and came over and stood nearby, and in my glances in her direction, I could see she was thoroughly amused. The tussle continued for a few more moments and then, in a coordinated dive, both mink leapt for the grayling, clamped down and tore it from Tim's fingers. In an instant we were all left there standing, watching empty space.

The woman looked up and said, "Well, boys, I haven't had entertainment like that for quite some time. Can I interest you in a green salad? From the looks of you, I'd say you haven't had one in quite a while."

I knew my brothers would agree with me when I replied, "Yes, ma'am. It *has* been a long time since we've eaten greens, and a salad sure sounds good." Tim and Ben were nodding furiously, and we all started joking about the mink as we followed her to her camper.

Her produce selection was complete, and beside the first lettuce we'd had in weeks, we devoured onions, green beans, and pickles, all washed down with V–8 juice. As we ate, we swapped travel stories, and she told us she'd been on the road about two months since her start back in Ontario.

I felt her trip was quite an accomplishment, as she looked to be in her sixties. She was slim and wiry, like she was used to living alone, with shoulder-length salt and pepper hair. She wore blue jeans and a cardigan, and her rubber boots had seen wear. She smiled a lot. I didn't know anyone back home in their sixties who would have undertaken such an adventure, even with company.

Driving tips for the roads we were traveling always came up between wanderers and often included points that weren't covered in the guidebooks.

"What do you do when you meet a large vehicle head on, on one of these single-track roads?" I asked her. "Lots of times, there's no room to pull off."

"Oh, I just make a rum runner," she answered casually.

"What's a rum runner?" we all questioned in unison.

"You don't know what a rum runner is? It's a turn-around boot leggers used to use to evade the Feds during prohibition. I'll show you if you like, but you'll have to help me put everything away and fasten anything down that's not already secure."

We did as she suggested while she hopped from the camper into the driver's seat and started the engine. We joined her, the four of us crammed up front.

"Let's pretend we were whiskey smugglers getting chased by a car full of agents. I'll do this in slow motion so as to keep the risk and the surprise to a minimum. The first thing I'd do as the driver if I thought they were gaining on us would be to pull as far over to the left as I could and stop, which, by itself, is a gutsy move when there's a car full of police closing in on you. This whole maneuver owes its success to being totally unexpected."

And then she did what she was describing, coming to a dead stop on the left hand side of the road. "Next, I'd make the second illogical maneuver—I'd start backing up, toward my pursuers. Not too fast, mind you, but enough to get a good momentum going, like this." She shifted into reverse and we turned towards the rear-view mirror, three of us in mounting anxiety. The elderly woman looked completely relaxed.

"By this time, the Feds would be close, sometimes so close they'd be too shocked to do anything except to slam on their brakes. So, now, still in reverse, I depress the clutch, gun the engine, then pop the clutch quickly to break the rear tires loose. Once they're spinning, I turn the wheel a bit to the right and then hard and all the way back to the left. With the rearward momentum and the rear tires spinning in reverse, the front end swings around like a pendulum and we've suddenly reversed direction."

All this she performed with such a fluid motion that the pickup swung backward in a beautifully smooth arc, with the scenery passing swiftly from right to left. The front end came around within the borders of the single lane, and as it passed the halfway point, she shifted from reverse to second, the truck now rolling in the opposite direction without losing a bit of momentum. It never even slowed down. She then braked to a halt and said, "That's a rum-runner, boys."

"And you're a marvel of stunt driving," Tim said. "I wouldn't want to be an agent chasing you."

"That's the thing about the rum-runner. Besides

accomplishing what it has to, there's also the advantage of its intimidation factor. You can reverse direction any time you want, smoothly and safely, but first you have to come to a complete stop."

There was silence while her words rang in my head. The tone of her voice and her lingering look at us implied something bigger, a metaphor maybe. I looked back at her, and suddenly, though I'm not sure she had meant to, I knew she was talking about a lot more than just turning a car around.

She was talking about the need we all have to change the direction of our lives, especially if we're being chased by demons. The first thing we have to do is come to a complete stop, even if it goes against all rational thought. And then, sometimes against every grain of our being, we have to turn and face our fear closely. The anxiety this generates motivates us, and our newfound confidence guides us through the change, albeit sometimes with tremors.

We thanked her for her gifts and her kindness and, after warm farewells and reminders to eat our vegetables, we headed up the road. We never did learn her name.

Chapter 15

The Alaskan border was about a tank of gas away and it had a postscript to add to what we'd learned from our newest friend. Five hours of driving later, in the drone of the broken exhaust, Ben sat up in the back seat and after some rustling with maps said, "You know, we should be hitting the Alaskan border pretty soon." And sure enough, within a couple of minutes, we saw the customs station approaching. We were over 5,500 miles from home. The agent asked the standard questions regarding the nature of our visit and if we had anything to declare. And with the all clear, we pulled out.

"Welcome to Alaska, guys," Tim said. "I'd say this occasion deserves some music." With that, he snapped on the knob on the broken radio and, pretending to keep the beat to an imaginary song, started drumming his hands on the metal dashboard. We were surprised to hear crackling static for a moment and then, dumbfounded, the driving rhythm of Led Zeppelin's lead singer, Robert Plant, wailing, "We come from the land of the ice and snow, from the midnight sun where the hot springs flow."

And then the radio went dead.

We stared at one another in silence. I smacked the dash in a lame attempt at revival, but we all knew it wasn't coming back. Those lyrics had played for us, as a triumphant hail to our arrival but also as a haunting reminder of the role of chance. We glanced at each other slack jawed.

"Great timing with your music selection, Tim," Ben said.

"There's a message in there somewhere, I think," he added.

"Up here, we're closer to the elemental forces of the earth. It could be a welcome, or a caution. Either way, prepare to be amazed," I said.

It was two hundred miles to Delta Junction, and another hundred further north to Fairbanks, all of which we made without incident. Except for a dead-end road, which traveled 150 miles northeast to the town of Circle, Fairbanks was the farthest north you could then get by car in North America and the official end of the AlCan Highway. As the end of the highway, Fairbanks was also the beginning of the rest of Alaska, which was itself the rest of the North American continent. North and west from here, roadless wilderness stretched for 500,000 square miles, about twice the size of Texas.

We arrived about a month after the summer solstice, when there was still over 21 hours of sunlight each day. Even after sunset, the twilight was bright enough to allow daytime activities. Here and elsewhere throughout this land of the midnight sun, we saw road crews working around the clock. The city hosts a popular midnight softball tournament, and farmers, who grow 100-pound cabbages in the long light, work day and "night." Residents take advantage of the long days to get as much done as possible before winter arrives, in September.

Sitting at the bottom of the Tanana Valley, Fairbanks has arctic air settling, sending temperatures frequently below -40° F. "Warm" air rises to the top of the hills north of town, while the city experiences one of the biggest temperature inversions on earth. The record low is -66° F. This extreme cold, which can last for days, often triggers a phenomenon common in Fairbanks but rare elsewhere—ice fog.

Below -40° F., with humidity near 100 percent, the air can no longer absorb moisture, so ice crystals form and hang suspended, like a cloud on the ground. You can feel the particles when you walk through them. Drivers often leave their cars running because starting them in this cold is so difficult, the result being thick clouds of toxic ice that form anywhere the idling vehicles are left, particularly in parking lots. Simply going from the warmth of life indoors outside into air this frigid can mean a temperature difference of 120 degrees, just by walking through a door, a shock your lungs struggle with. The average high temperature in January is still below zero degrees Fahrenheit. Accompanying the cold is the darkness. At the winter solstice, Fairbanks gets 3 hours and 43 minutes of sunlight. But as if to offset this deprivation, the aurora borealis is visible more than 200 nights a year.

We were glad we'd arrived in July and for the chance to finally repair the exhaust correctly and to replenish our stocks of oatmeal, peanut butter, tuna, and bread. We were also excited about the possibility of taking a bush plane into the arctic, but dropped the hope when a quoted fare came in at more than we could afford. The price was reasonable, considering airplane maintenance, pilot experience, and fuel costs. The pilot had to make two round-trip flights, one to drop us off and another to pick us up three days later. But the price represented most of the money we had left.

Fortunately, our disappointment didn't last long, because Mt. McKinley, the highest mountain in North America and the only one over 20,000 feet, was, by Alaskan standards (120 miles), just down the road. This time it wasn't the fishing that drew us. It was the view.

On a scale with the land it's a part of, Denali National Park occupies an area larger than the state of Massachusetts. We pulled over just inside the park gate to study the map the ranger gave us.

With Ben leaning over from the back seat, three heads pondered the map.

"Okay, so the farthest we can drive in on the park road is to Savage Lake, about fifteen miles," Ben said. "From there, we have to board the public bus, which takes us in to the mining camp at Kantishna, ninety-one miles from here. Where do we want to go?"

"I don't know about you guys, but I'd like to get a good view of McKinley. From the photo of the mountain from Wonder Lake, that seems like a good spot to aim for," I said.

"Maybe," Tim said. "It also says that older expeditions used to approach the mountain from McGonagall Pass, before they started flying in to one of the mountain's glaciers. McGonagall Pass looks like a hike of about twenty-five miles, over Muldrow Glacier. The pass could give us a great view."

"That might take us three days, but we just resupplied. We've got plenty of food," Ben added.

"It also says that Eielson Visitor Center is the closest the park road gets to McKinley," I said. "The old expedition route looks close to Eielson. We could jump off from there."

"Well, arctic fishing was a bust, but we can give ourselves this adventure," Ben said. "I say let's do it."

"Sounds like a plan to me," Tim said.

After camping a night at Savage Lake, we caught the 3:00 p.m. park bus and rode four hours and 50 miles further in. The road hugs a line of hills on the north, with spectacular views east and south paralleling the Alaska Range. Along the way, the driver provided commentary on what we were looking at: treeless, rolling tundra with small patches of scrub willow and spruce. He described the environmental conditions that create such a landscape, including the glaciation, the short growing season, and brutal cold and wind. Because there is very little actual soil and the permafrost prevents root penetration, the earth, with few exceptions, can support only the growth of mosses, grasses, and flowers. He stopped the bus for a few minutes while we watched a foraging grizzly, but we kept looking at the highest peak in the range we paralleled, impressed with its looming height and mass. It was taller and bigger than any mountain we'd seen so far. But the driver didn't mention it, making us wonder if we'd been looking at McKinley.

The bus contoured the hillsides, and curved through Polychrome Pass, 46 miles in, named for its multicolored bluffs. We got off at Eielson, a small building with a single room and a set of bathrooms. A large display in the center of the room, covered with plexiglass, showcased a map of the park. The single, wraparound window provided a 180–degree view of the Alaska Range in the distance and what the map told us was the McKinley Bar in the foreground. The Bar was the flat, alluvial plain in front of and below us, threaded with braids of runoff streams from Muldrow Glacier. We were the only visitors.

The ranger watched us check out the map and compare it to the view out the window.

"What are you fellows planning? Perhaps I can answer

questions you might have." He was tall and trim in his uniform and spoke with the ease of someone who's spent time both helping tourists and rescuing people in the backcountry.

"We'd like to hike to McGonagall Pass, on the old route over Muldrow Glacier. We want to get a view of McKinley that not many others see," Tim said.

"It is a great view from the pass. And not many hikers get that far," he said. "There are no trails, but there are a couple of routes. Let me show you on this park map and then we can locate them on your topographic map."

He pointed out the huge window to the features we'd landmark, and then found them on both maps. Finding the route seemed, if not easy, at least logical, and as we reviewed the maps, the steps to the pass took shape. From the encouraging way he spoke, the hike seemed within our ability.

"How's the summer here been so far?" I asked.

"About the usual," he said. "A team of climbing rangers recovered three bodies from a failed Japanese expedition a couple of weeks ago. There was also a climbing party trapped on the mountain for two weeks by storms. It was tense for a while, but they got off okay. Another climber fell into a covered crevasse when a snow bridge collapsed and was rescued by his partner. And not far from here, a bear mauled a ranger last week. It took him three days to crawl to the park road, but he's going to be all right." He related all this matter of factly, as seasonal routine. For him, it was.

For us, it wasn't so every day, although our concern didn't translate into realistic assessment of our goal, something the ranger had perhaps been subtly trying to get us to do. Up to now, we'd hiked on well-worn trails to our goals, using maps to confirm our location on the trail or the trail's direction. Without a path, we'd be leaning heavily on our orienteering skills and good weather. Yet we were assuming we'd bushwhack 25 miles of challenging terrain unknown to us, with only a map and compass, and arrive at McGonagall Pass.

"I guess there's a lot to be aware of, even just hiking. Thanks for the heads up. And thanks a lot for your help with our route," Tim said.

"You're welcome. You should be fine—the forecast is favorable and it's a great hike. Let's hope the view is clear. You might get lucky. Have a good hike, guys," he replied.

"Thanks."

Our first mistake was not gauging the scale of what we saw out the window by simply comparing it to our map. Muldrow Glacier was our first destination and also the route we'd follow to the pass. It rose to the north, beyond what seemed like a short distance across the McKinley Bar. The Bar looked like a flat, expansive valley floor of black sand woven with dozens of twisted streams from the glacier, that joined and separated in a pattern of intertwining filaments.

We knew the streams would be cold, and we just assumed they'd be shallow. To the base of the glacier, across the Bar, it looked like a twenty–minute hike. It was only 7:30, and with at least four hours of light left, we'd have plenty of time to cross it, make camp, and have a leisurely, if late, dinner.

We headed down slope to the Bar. It was much farther down than we'd thought and when we finally pushed our way through the willows at the bottom and stepped onto the Bar's edge, it began to dawn on us just how wide this flat was. The black "sand" we'd seen from above was indeed black, but it was gravel, not sand, and it was sharp and pointed. No rounded river stones here; this rock had just been ground by the glacier. The first stream looked shallow, although we couldn't be sure because the water was gray with sediment. We removed our boots and socks, hitched up our pant cuffs, and waded in.

With the first step, the water rose to our knees, but the stream was narrow and it didn't get any deeper. Even crossing a flow that narrow, however, the cold numbed our feet and legs. Replacing our socks and boots, we marched to the next stream, where we repeated the process. Only this time, the water climbed to our thighs and we could feel the sand under our soles being swept away by the current. We lurched to keep our balance with full packs, and the frigid water rose on our upstream side until we finally clambered out onto the bank. Our bruised and frozen feet welcomed the dry socks and boots, but we knew the comfort was short-lived. Crossing the endless number of streams we were looking at across the flat in this fashion would take days. Dry boots were not an option.

At the next stream, we plunged into the current with our boots on and were actually glad to have protected feet. We were wet again and again as we forded stream after stream, a few times getting in to our waists. And although we were resigned now to the icy slog and didn't even hesitate at each stream bank, the far side of the bar didn't seem any closer. At this point, we'd been out a lot longer than the half hour we'd thought it would take. We were miserable, but at least not bleeding, and the sun was still shining. Too far across to turn back and with no place near to just give up and pitch camp, we kept marching. If we just kept going, we'd eventually get there, or so I told myself.

We must have all been thinking the same thing because no

one was speaking. Even with all the exertion and wearing two tee shirts and a sweatshirt, the repeated dunkings were making me colder and my fingers were turning white. I was thankful there wasn't a wind, but even without it, Ben's lips were going blue. Despite this, his eyes held conviction and he strode with confidence. Tim's teeth were clenched with determination, as if the struggle had become personal. But he too walked strongly into stream after stream. Their countenances buoyed my resolve, and the whining I was contemplating changed into if not exactly confidence at least encouragement.

The streams would surprise us with their depth, so we learned to take the first step in with caution and swapped the lead taking that first step. Without the usual riverbank debris lying around, there weren't any wading staffs available, so we had to keep our balance in the current with arms extended, sometimes flailing wildly. Graceful I was not, but the object was to avoid a swim. We'd all unhitched our waist belts by now, just in case we did go under, but at the least, falling in would mean wet gear, including clothes and sleeping bags. At the worst, we might lose the pack completely and be unable to recover it in the current. Still not a life–threatening situation perhaps, but one that explained the look of concentration on our faces while crossing and the expression of relief when stepping out.

Even though it was now pushing 10:00 p.m. and we hadn't eaten since lunch, no one mentioned food. Without trees or other nearby features of vertical relief, it was hard to gauge our progress, and for what felt like an eternity we didn't seem to be making any. We were adrift on a flat sea of rock and streams at the mercy of an immense scale we'd stupidly not accounted for. In the depths of a blunder this deep, you can count on only two things: luck and endurance. Fortunately, our luck kept the skies clear and the wind to a gentle breeze. And our well of youthful strength was deep enough to sustain us. Just before midnight, we stepped off the McKinley Bar onto a hill of tundra grass leading up to the glacier's moraine.

A celebration was in order, but we were too spent for jubilance. Besides, just as I looked up at Tim to share congratulations, his head was enveloped in a massive cloud of mosquitoes. I looked at Ben, but he'd also disappeared in a swarm of his own. And then it was my turn.

We needed to get to high ground right away, where a wind, or even a breeze, would help keep the bugs at bay.

"Let's get to the top of this hill!" Tim shouted, coughing on a mouthful of mosquitoes. Despite our fatigue, we trudged up the slope of sand and rock, glad for the warmth the exertion provided. On the steep pitch, we slid back nearly as much as each step forward and tried to step in each other's prints to reduce the slippage. Our boots filled with sand and gravel, scouring our ankles, but the mosquitoes kept us climbing. The higher we got, the stronger the breeze became, until, when we finally reached the crest, it had become a light wind. Thinned only marginally, the insects still swarmed and we still flailed. It was time to camp and eat and rest, the sooner the better.

No one said anything as we tore the tent, sleeping bags, and mats from our packs in the hail of whining parasites. The tent was pitched and filled in record time. We threw ourselves in last, zipped the door, and removed our gravel-filled boots. Lighting a stove to cook dinner meant going outside, so dinner was cold—peanut butter and jelly, a can of sardines, and Tang. Even getting this simple task completed with all of our gear inside was a slow-motion affair in close quarters, with frequent delays to swat bugs that had gotten inside, but we all finally got settled in our bags and were starting to warm up.

Lying there, packed together, we were staring up at the orange rip-stop roof of the tent only a few inches away from our faces. The sun shining through it, combined with the tent fly luffing in the wind, made it glow with a warmth that was lulling us to sleep. Gradually, though, the roof got darker and darker until it was nearly completely blackened. Our hordes were back. We could hear them ticking the nylon as they poked the roof trying to get to us, a million pinpricks. "Oh my God," Ben muttered. "This is insane."

"Watch this," Tim said, as he flicked the roof with his finger. A circle of darkness a foot in diameter exploded into light and the whining red-lined; then the area immediately began to darken as the swarm descended again.

"Great material for an Alfred Hitchcock movie," Ben said.

"Yeah," Tim agreed. "Reminds me of that short story, 'Leiningen and the Ants,' only these bugs can fly."

"I've never been so grateful for a thirty-secondth of an inch of rip-stop nylon," Ben said. "We're the specimens now and they're doing the examining."

"More like the sampling," I said. "It's really frightening when you realize that what's out there is only half the population."

""What do you mean?" Tim asked.

"Only the female mosquitoes suck blood," I reminded him. "The males live on nectar and plant juices. Mosquitoes live only a couple of weeks, which explains why these females are so pushy. They need a blood meal to reproduce, and they're running out of time."

"I hate to bother you with so many questions, Mr. Science Guy, but how do they find us so quickly?" Ben asked.

"They're drawn to the carbon dioxide we exhale. And our sweat," he said.

"Oh, great. All we have to do is stop breathing and moving and they'll look elsewhere. Fat chance. And all the DEET in the world isn't going to work against these hordes, either," Ben said.

"It might help, but our best hope is for a strong wind," I said.

Tim jumped in. "Yeah, well, let's hope for a hurricane, guys."

Chapter 16

Dawn was long past by the time we stirred the next morning, which was a bonus we hadn't planned on. The mosquitoes seemed slightly less numerous in the bright sun, and although the wind made starting the stove difficult, the hot bowl of oatmeal, raisins, and brown sugar made the struggle worthwhile. We gulped strong tea, boiled in the same pot the oatmeal had been cooked in, rolled and packed the tent and the bags and were ready to hike quickly.

The slope up the moraine mirrored the one we'd descended from the visitor's center to the Bar the evening before, a slurry of sand and gravel that slid back with every step up. Nearing the top, I felt strange looking back at our starting point. While crossing it, the Bar was immense. With the perspective of distance, what we'd spent the last six hours traversing was now a minute part of our view. Thinking ahead towards McGonagall Pass, I began to recalibrate my conception of our goal. Given the shock to our senses the Bar had surprised us with, was a hike to the pass realistic? Perhaps it was time to apply the lessons of the rum–runner.

In less than half an hour we were up on the glacier itself, and the strange shock of it looked nothing like the wide, white band on our topographic map. It was an undulating version of the McKinley Bar, a vast expanse of rolling and pitching swells of black basalt. The glacier was covered with the till it had scoured from the terrain—dinner-plate-size flakes of volcanic rock. Ice, not the expected snow, lay just below this layer, so each step was a teetering, sliding shift underfoot. The immense pressure of the glacier's mass buckled and heaved the surface into mountains of giant, sharp chips, which we had to climb periodically to get our bearings. We learned not to hike too close together, to prevent the mosquitoes from combining, and to keep moving in order to compound the benefit of the wind.

The sun rose to its zenith quickly and stayed there, seemingly forever. We'd take a step from one skittering chip to the next, whirling our arms wildly under the loads of our backpacks, grateful when the surface was solid. The combination of heavy packs and the lurching and lunging on heaps of finely edged rock ground our boot soles and softened their support. Our ankles weakened. Progress over the glacier was slow.

We ate lunch standing up, passing around the bag of gorp, the can of sardines, and the bottle of Tang, and gaping at the view. The Alaska Range ran for miles east to west in front of us, mostly shrouded by clouds. Of those peaks we could see, there was that one peak taller than the rest we'd seen from the bus. But just knowing we were getting closer than anyone who rode a bus on the park road made me feel privileged. We'd come thousands of miles to allow ourselves the chance to do just this, and we were, despite considerable discomforts and some real hazards, fulfilling our intent. As tired and as battered as I was, I felt good. I also felt rich, in the same way you do when you fully understand you'll never return to this place or this time.

"Well, guys, there it is. The highest peak in the Western

hemisphere," Tim said, through chomps on his gorp. "It would be nice if the clouds lifted, but the view is spectacular just the same. That's higher than any peak we've seen so far or any we're going to see. Measured from its base, which is much closer to sea level than the base of Mt. Everest, McKinley is higher."

While still swatting hordes of mosquitoes, we gazed at the peak, the lodestone of our compass. I was trying to imagine what it would be like to climb it, and could see why it drew mountaineers from all over the world. Its status as the highest peak in North America was the primary reason. But among climbers, it is also acknowledged as a far more difficult climb than peaks of equal height in South America or even Nepal, because of its latitude. Besides sharing the usual hazards of avalanches and crevasses as well as a difficult approach through remote and dangerous terrain, Denali is known for its cold. Even during the height of the arctic summer, temperatures often fall well below zero and, combined with a nearly constant wind, make climbing extremely difficult. Only five years prior to our visit, in 1967, Denali had been the site of what, up until then, had been the third worst disaster in mountaineering in terms of lives lost. Seven of 12 climbers perished while stranded for 10 days near the summit, in what has been described as the worst storm on record.

This was before the surge in big mountain expeditions in the 1980s and 1990s, when climbing status peaks became a niche business. More and more wealthy people with less climbing experience began to fuel a market that standardized approaches and routes as well as supply lines. To shorten the approach to Denali, and the total time to reach the summit, climbers were flown in over much of the approach from the airstrip in Talkeetna to the Kahiltna Glacier, right on the mountain itself. Similar measures were taken on other major peaks to meet the needs of these less qualified mountaineers. Fixed ropes were established, as well as ladders, and the need for bottled oxygen mushroomed. With these aids, clients had less time to acclimate to the altitude.

The fixed ropes, ladders, and oxygen bottles needed replacement, but they weren't always carried out after they'd been taken in, and dump sites for discarded equipment began to appear at high altitudes on mountains, and grew with each climbing season. Over 16 tons of garbage has been removed from Everest since 2008, with 50 tons still remaining on the mountain.

The use of satellite phones and helicopters also increased efficiency and success rates as more customers with less and less experience were put within reach of major summits. Technology and wealth had made ascents of the earth's major peaks a new fashion and behavior statement, much as promenades and automobiles had for the well-to-do at the posh hotels of the 1920s. The rising graph line of advanced technology in climbing equipment and the falling line of clients' conditioning and actual climbing skill eventually led to a number of high-profile mountaineering failures in which many clients and their guides lost their lives. Risk had finally been pressed to its extreme as the vapor of hubris and wealth replaced the substance of judgment and experience.

We kept moving, separated by the need to keep our personal clouds of mosquitoes apart. The distance prevented conversation that might have kept our spirits up, and we were left to cope in isolation with the misery underfoot and overhead. We spoke only when we stopped to rest or when we needed to check the map. At one such map check, I slapped one of my shoulders with my opposite hand, then looked at my palm and counted seventeen bloody mosquito corpses. This was through a tee shirt and a sweatshirt.

"I'm about ready to jump off a cliff to end this torture, except then you guys would feel obliged to carry my body back," Ben said.

"Well, don't be so sure," I replied, smiling. "Right now, you're more valuable to us as the mule for the food, stove, and tent you're hauling. And remember," I added, "Whatever you do, you don't lose the mule." I could barely see his eyes through the mosquitoes.

"I will say this for the caribou, though," Tim added. "They may migrate for food and for calving grounds, but they're sure as hell also moving to stay ahead of this insanity. These critters are driving me crazy."

I was sitting down at this point to check my boots, which had begun to feel more like bedroom slippers, and discovered that the vibram soles were ripped open. At the rate they were deteriorating, I was afraid to think how soon I'd be walking barefoot over this terrain. Blisters were an accepted hazard, but complete boot failure was a scary prospect.

"Ben, what time does your watch say? My stomach says we should have had dinner by now," I shouted, wildly swatting the whining cloud.

"It's nine o'clock, believe it or not. Let's find a place to camp and fix a hot meal," he replied. Without another word, we headed for the highest point nearby, which though not exactly on our route, was higher than anything else around. The wind there would help reduce the mosquito density, and when we arrived, we found a surprise bonus, a number of discarded wooden expedition crates. We immediately built a fire, which further repelled the bugs and softened our misery.

Our pot had a plastic handle, which would have melted over the open fire, so we had to use our back–packing stove to heat the beans. But try as it might in the wind, the poor stove's flame was no match for the gusts. Tim and Ben pitched the tent, laid out the bags inside, and were anxious to eat. Watching the pot wasn't helping. And even though they were thinned by the wind, the mosquitoes, now that we weren't moving, had stationary annoyance honed to the point of distraction. When someone said, "Let's just eat them, warm or not," no one objected, so I spooned them out into three metal dishes.

That's when we realized the mosquitoes had been waiting too. They dove into our plates with such fury that we were suddenly picking dead bugs from our meals in a losing battle for our food. In no time, the futility of this defense became apparent. In the time it took to pluck one from the gooey morass, many others would glue themselves to the meal. Surrender was the only sane response, and we madly shoveled the beans, and their mosquito garnish, into our mouths. The way I figured it, we could use the extra protein.

We left the dishes for the morning, dove into our tent and breathed a giant, collective sigh of relief. Just getting horizontal had never felt so good.

The morning brought a surprise none of us had expected. We'd gotten the stove going, and the oatmeal was bubbling when Tim said, "Hey guys, the clouds are moving off the range. And the mountains showing are higher than the one we thought was Mt. McKinley." Ben and I both turned to watch the slowly shifting cloudbank and the rising elevation of the skyline. It was true. The peaks that were appearing were much higher than the one we'd figured was "The High One."

We were all standing now, gazing silently toward the range. The mosquitoes swarmed. The oatmeal burned. The wind blew. And the 15 miles of Muldrow Glacier stretched out in chunks-of-asphalt fashion toward McGonagall Pass. Up and up we lifted our heads as the clouds drifted off. And we still stood in silence, awestruck by the single remaining peak that consumed the horizon.

The change was so radically different as to be disorienting. This one, freshly revealed mountain, with a flag of snow flying from its peak, now so totally filled our view that the scale of the topography around us was radically altered. The last shard of glass in the kaleidoscope had fallen into place and, with that change, the image was no longer even of the same dimension.

Everything had changed. The sudden wave of reverence was so strong there were no words for it. Here was the Pacific Plate, a layer of earth ten miles thick, in head-on collision with the North American Plate. The violence of that collision was unimaginable, but the serenity of the result was completely absorbing.

"Jesus," Ben murmured. "Now I know why we came." There was a long pause. I waited for Tim to say something. But he didn't, and neither did I.

After a lengthy, silent homage, we slowly turned back to the tent. With a lot of scraping we got a decent pot of oatmeal served. The tea with oatmeal scum tasted great, the sun was shining, and the wind was helping to keep the bugs at bay. We all faced the mountain while we slurped the gruel, just gazing.

Chapter 17

Even though we were somewhat refreshed from a night's sleep, the two days of struggling over a harsh landscape, with the constant cloud of mosquitoes, had taken its toll. We were beat and bitten, and our boot soles were ready for the I.C.U. And probably because we thought we might get to that point also, we decided it was time to turn back. We'd seen what we came to see, and getting to the pass wasn't going to make the view of Mt. McKinley that much greater, not enough anyway to make the additional slog worth it.

Looking at the topographic map, I said, "So what do you guys think? We could retrace our steps. But, from here, the map shows a shorter route to the park road, although it brings us out on the road a ways from the visitor center."

"I'd rather walk on road, instead of the glacier or the moraine, even it's a little longer. I don't know how long my boots are going to hold up," Ben said.

"Walking on the road is faster than hiking the moraine or the glacier, too," Tim added. "Let's give it a try."

So after breaking camp, we set off, topo in hand, for what the map called the East Fork, which we needed to cross.

The familiarity of the sliding chips of black rock, thinly layered over a base of ice, returned quickly, and we staggered our way over the swells. The mosquitoes returned just as fast, and we swatted and flailed, catching our balance with every step. I was glad we'd decided to head back and was pretty sure my brothers were thinking the same thing. We knew what we were facing now; we just wished it wasn't going to last so long.

Tim was in the lead, I was following, and Ben was trailing. We were hiking up one of the infinite number of slopes on the glacier and Tim was out ahead when he shouted down to us, "Guys! Come up and take a look at this, but be careful as you get close." I was curious and even more so as I got closer and he said, "Now go slow and be really careful."

I inched forward and suddenly was looking over the rim of a crater maybe a 100 feet across. The edge fell down dirty ice in a steep-walled funnel about 30 feet to a sight so frightening I immediately took a step back.

The whirlpool of churning black water gnawed at the base of the ice, carving an undercut that echoed with an ominous grinding. Refrigerator-sized chunks were breaking off and joining the swirling current. If you fell in, there'd be no way you could get out or be rescued. It would be a horrible death, as the freezing water paralyzed your panicked thrashing until you sank. I inched backward and Ben came up. "Go easy, Ben," I said. "This is really scary." He looked concerned, but also as though he doubted anything could be as spooky as my voice, until he peeked over the brim and gasped. He stepped back right away.

"What is this?" he asked. "This is the scariest god-damn thing I've ever seen," he added. "If you ever fell in there—"

"Yeah, we know," I broke in.

As if identifying it would banish my fear I added, "I think it's a sinkhole where a crevasse in the glacier has opened to the river of runoff below. There's more water entering than there is leaving, maybe because of constricted flow, and the backed-up water begins to spin."

"Which means," Tim said, there might be channels eroded by the flow from underneath that are covered only by thin bridges. It's pretty scary to think what might be ready to break through just by walking on it."

"Guys, we'd better watch our step," I said. "We should take turns in the lead, just in case. I wish we had a rope."

We stood there, riveted by the fear of "what if" until, having had enough, I began to edge back down. Tim and Ben got their last looks and joined me on the slope below. I realized I was breathing a lot easier, grateful to have survived a look into the abyss. Tim and Ben looked a lot lighter too.

We resumed our slippery progress, stopping occasionally to check the map or munch gorp. The weather seemed to be holding, and we ate a standing lunch again to save time and shorten our distance from the East Fork. The hours wore on, so we were glad when we finally made it to the river. But satisfaction with our route finding was immediately smothered by new information. We couldn't cross.

We'd intersected the East Fork right where it shot from the base of the glacier in a blast so strong we could hear boulders cracking underwater. Haystacks three feet high frothed and fell in the main current. The water was so black, we couldn't tell how deep it was, but that didn't matter anyway. If you stepped in it, the current would flush you instantly. After our experience with the glacial black hole, the scope of potential and probable negatives had gotten magnitudes darker. The roar drowned our voices.

Pointing up at the wall of ice where the East Fork erupted, I yelled, "No way we're going to climb that. Way too steep."

"Let's look for a way above or around it," Ben suggested. "Getting across is going to shorten our return by a lot."

So we searched. We tramped downstream for a while, but the East Fork raced without slowing for as far as we could see. Upstream, the terrain around the ice wall was cleaved with crevasses. Crossing wasn't going to be possible.

The sting of this reality was made even more painful by knowing that from the other side, our route back to the park road was shorter by miles. I looked at our boots and worried about them, then at my brothers' faces and worried about all of us.

"At least we know our way back," I said. And we've got enough food for a couple of days."

"That's some consolation," Ben said. "But I'd love to cross that stream."

"Wouldn't we all," Tim said.

Our only choice was to backtrack. Once resigned to this, we despondently dragged ourselves up the slope toward the rolling swells of the glacier and the previous night's camp. We had a standing dinner and kept plodding. Having already been where we were headed, we were able to straighten our path somewhat and cut some distance off our return. Our stumbling pace was quickened by a new climate of frustration that drove us on.

By about 6:30, we made it to our former camp. Though tempted to camp again, our unsuccessful bid to cross the East Fork and shorten our trek had spawned a sense of last–ditch effort to get ourselves out of what we'd gotten ourselves into. Patience was a rapidly disappearing commodity. With tempers festering, volatility was peaking.

Sometimes it really is better to do nothing; the rum–runner, hounded by the federal agents, maintains the focus to first come to a complete stop. The pause would have let us catch our breath and maintain control of our pace. But in a rush to fix our situation now, we pressed on.

Too busy coping with our misery, no one said anything. One step in front of another, with the clacking plates of black basalt for company, we trudged the swells of our now detested glacier. Our determination, however blind, focused our effort, and we made it across the glacier to the scrub willows waiting at the edge of the tundra. We broke out some biscuits and sardines in a weak attempt to celebrate but cut the party short when it began to rain hard. The bush was shoulder high or sometimes taller and crisscrossed with knee–deep streams, prime bear habitat. I remembered the ranger who'd been mauled in the area and tried to make as much noise as I could. If bears hear you before they see you, they'll move off. We'd seen plenty of bears, and now was not the time for a close encounter. There were signs—huge tracks in the sand by the creeks, willows bent or sometimes crushed in the path of a large mammal—but they didn't look fresh. We didn't see any recent kills or scat, either.

But I wasn't taking any chances and began singing, in as loud a voice as I could muster in the rain. It didn't matter what—rock and roll tunes, folksongs, nursery rhymes. Whatever came into my head was next on the play list. Tim and Ben caught on to what I was up to and joined me; we began to take turns with new songs. We mocked our rock and folk heroes, exaggerating the lyrics or even parodying them. It became a game to invent a clever, funny, raunchy, or just plain stupid verse.

We were tired and hungry. Our boots were disintegrating. A cold rain drenched us as we beat and whacked and grunted our way through thickets and across streams. Mosquitoes were checked somewhat by the rain, but still perforated our soaked clothing and uncovered skin. Ben's boots fell apart, the soles open and catching on the brush. But he kept singing. Tim carried the heaviest pack, but he too kept charging into the brush, singing the dumbest, most nonsensical verses he could contrive, sometimes even in time with his lunges at the walls of brush. His high school days as a lineman on the football team returned, with furious hits at the brush from his lowered shoulder. His grimace, through twisted lyrics, took on a demonic glow.

My pack had no waist belt, and with all the weight on my shoulders, my neck was a bundle of knotted pain. But we three were sharing our misery, and shared misery differs from solo suffering in that, together, the struggles serve as a vehicle for bonding, sometimes to the point of displacing the importance of an external goal. Adversity becomes the base from which members deepen their connection. It is the prerequisite raw material for affirmation of our identity and satisfies the craving we have to know that we make a difference in the world.

Our response to challenge is our soul's measure of our worth. It is the rare individual who knows this and, incredibly, under impossible conditions, is smiling. We think this person must be crazy, or is woefully confident in the outcome, but this is a mistake. They smile because they are confident in their will. They know the outcome is out of their control, and they've accepted that. But they also know they will withhold nothing. The actual outcome becomes secondary. They measure themselves on this internal scale.

Our scales were synchronized in our brotherhood, and we made smooth, if slow, progress. But when the willow thickets ended and we suddenly faced the task of crossing, yet again, the seven miles of the McKinley Bar stretching out in front of us, we knew we'd completed only the first stage of our return. We were about to establish the depth of our will.

Chapter 18

Despite our despair, we knew we had some advantages. For one, we weren't fooled by the deceptive scale and now knew just how long this crossing took. For another, we were so soaked, torn, and bitten by this point that another round with the McKinley Bar wasn't going to preserve anything. So we plunged in, splashing our way across the first set of frigid streams, heedless now of any attempt to stay dry.

With the rainfall and the streams underfoot, we moved through a watery world. Our wet clothing absorbed all the rain it could, and then drained to our boots. The rain kept falling and we kept moving, switching off the lead as we tackled stream after stream of meandering, glacial melt water. Four hours later, we left the McKinley Bar behind and braced ourselves for the final push up the mountain to the road above. The exertion of the ascent warmed us and drained us at the same time; when we crested the last rise, it was nearly midnight. Astonishingly, there were lights on at the visitor's center and idling buses were parked outside.

My brothers looked like phantoms, skeletal waifs dragged from the storm surf of the McKinley Bar. Ben's white face was smeared with soaked locks of long, filthy, red hair strewn with willow leaves and twigs. His blood shot eyes were sunken and hollow and his hands were covered with scratches, a few of which were bleeding. Tim's bloodless fingers were shredded with nicks and tears and he had a long cut across his ear, which bled in minute rills onto his jaw. His sweatshirt was torn at the neck, where a cluster of debris had collected. Through the open tear at one knee of his pant leg, blood fanned out across skin. Both pairs of their boots were spitting gravel and water.

Both of them were smiling.

Remembering my college study of Tennyson, I suddenly understood in a visceral way another meaning of the phrase, "when I have crost the bar."

We asked about a ride out, but the buses were for a late-returning private tour. The warm and dry visitor's center felt wonderful, and we cooked dinner right on the cement floor. In the last seventeen hours of travel on foot, navigating with map and compass, over moraine and glacier and through countless streams, we'd covered over 26 miles.

All of our gear was soaked, including the sleeping bags. Despite this, Ben and Tim dropped off to sleep right away. I was too tired to sleep and the wheels in my head kept turning, mostly with the question of where I was headed next. I could now envision the end of this trip, whenever it came. Tim would be headed back to his house painting, and Ben had to return to school. My future was a mystery wrapped in confusion and indecision.

I now held a college degree and had even graduated cum laude, but I still had no burning vision of what I wanted to do. I liked the idea of teaching, but to get certified I'd have to return to school. And though I liked student life, I'd dedicated every penny of the many jobs I'd had to pay my way. I also needed a change from the academic world and wanted to see what the "real" world held. And even though I didn't know how I might best fulfill my potential and my life, I knew where I wanted to start, and it wasn't in the suburban world I'd come from.

That world was inhabited by established players, mostly men, who'd spent their lives building careers in New York and were still commuting to the city every day. They'd leave before sunrise and return after dark, sometimes staying over if work ran late. I remember summer evening Little League, when the bleachers would fill toward the end of the game with dads in white shirts and ties having just arrived from the train station to see the last few outs of their sons' game.

Our dad—Tamsen's, Tim's and mine—wasn't among them, having died when I was three and Tim younger. He'd been in advertising in the 1950s, when advertisers were beginning to sponsor programs in the new technology of television, and had joined the production team of "The Lucky Strike Hit Parade," a prime-time show on a major network. With everyone just figuring it all out, the hours were long and sometimes he'd sleep over in the city. He was working when Tim was born and didn't get to the hospital.

There was a lot of drinking in that world, and he'd been aware of his own excesses, which his mother had expressed concerns about also. One night, riding home from the city, he'd left the train two stops early, too ill to continue, and was taken to the hospital. It was never really clear what he died of. Mom said it was pneumonia, but in a way that seemed she wasn't totally sure herself.

Most of the photos I've seen of them together have booze and cigarettes in the frame as well, and I figured they'd been drinking partners. Given that Mom was an active alcoholic through my college years, this is probably pretty accurate. Maybe she knew more about his death but didn't want to say. To a young son, pneumonia sounds better than alcoholism. In my mind, I'd formed a vague combination of causes that included overwork and alcohol. He was 38 years old.

Most of the fathers we knew in our neighborhood were pursuing their careers with similar degrees of absence from family life. A couple of other commuting fathers I knew also died prematurely, but many just weren't around. Of the three closest friends I had in high school, guys whose houses I visited at least twice a week, I met only two of their fathers. When they were around, which was usually on the weekends, cocktail parties and gatherings at the country club consumed their time. The work/family imbalance bankrupted everyone. Even in the confusion of not knowing what I wanted, I knew that was one life I didn't want.

Mom remarried three years later to Ben Sr., a man from that same sphere who'd recently been divorced, and Ben Jr. was born a year later. Ben Sr. and Mom drank together, and their consumption increased. I was resistant to this new guy trying to be my father, despite some awkward attempts on his part to bridge the gap. He took a second mortgage on our house for capital to start his own advertising company, but the business failed and within three years he left to return to his former wife.

Our household now had three boys and one girl without a father. It also had a mother with a drinking problem, but without a job, facing a pile of debt. In middle school, we'd often come home to Mom passed out in bed, the empty vodka bottle on the floor.

Her mother, Grace, found out what was going on and came down from Vermont to straighten out her daughter and her daughter's family. As well intended as Grace was, her rigid stance only triggered increasingly explosive screaming matches between us all. We'd run to our rooms and lock the door, thinking we were safe. But a chair crashing through the door, wielded by Mom or Grandma, would launch us out the window and down the trees close to the house.

Lots of times we'd run from the house to escape the madness. We'd grab our fishing rods on the way out, hop on our bikes, and pedal off. The river or the pond were the places we could always go where we wouldn't be bothered, where we didn't need anything, and where the pursuit of fish helped us forget our home life. It was the fun we had there exploring, discovering, and coping that kept us sane. The older we got, the farther we went, until we knew every inch of both rivers in town from their reservoir sources in the north to the town line in the south.

Exploring a river was like finding a really deep friend: the more you knew, the more you wanted to know. Alhough it didn't always give you fish, the river would always fill your need. Whatever fish it gave you were welcomed for their wildness, their determination to fight, and their cleverness in escaping. They held their lives as dearly as we held ours, and our connection through the line mirrored those fights. In the way they knew best, the fish kept telling us to never give up. And with the adults in our world disabled, their voices were the strongest ones we heard.

Chapter 19

The guys woke early, and our unspoken consensus was that we'd seen plenty of the park, its animals and the mountain. We didn't need to go all the way to Wonder Lake, another 20 miles in, the traditional spot for viewing the mountain. We were ready to leave and find some dry comfort. So when a park bus returning from Wonder Lake surprised us at 7:00 a.m. and had room, we threw our gear together and piled on. After a three-hour ride out, we got off at the train depot in Savage Lake, where we'd parked our car. We lay down on the platform in the sun and fell fast asleep.

Two hours later, we hit the road headed south and discovered, to our dismay, that it was gravel. The car must have relaxed with the few miles of paved road we'd driven since Fairbanks because the return to dirt prompted immediate effects.

Within just a few miles, we hit a pothole and the exhaust suddenly became deafening. "What the hell!" Tim shouted.

"Don't look now, but I think that's our muffler behind us," Ben deadpanned, as Tim pulled over.

"We've got some wire, right?" I asked.

"Somewhere in the trunk. Good luck finding it," Ben said.

I rummaged for a while, found the wire, and Tim and I took

turns under the car, either holding the muffler in place or wiring it to anything solid. When we emerged, 20 minutes later, our hands were ochre from pipe rust, our hair was caked with grime, and we squinted at each other through eyes filled with dirt. Even after we brushed off each other's clothes, they were still filthy.

"Oh boy, I can't wait to do that again," Tim said.

"Don't worry, we can't. We're out of wire," I quipped. "Silver lining, you know."

The repair quieted the exhaust some, but we still had to shout.

Ten miles down the gravel, we hit another pothole and the driver's window dropped like a guillotine, lost into the door.

"Well, at least we didn't hear any shattering glass," Tim joked, still driving. "The crank spins like a compass needle. Let's live with it for now. I don't feel like stopping again."

"Okay with me," I yelled back. On we rolled.

There were many large trucks on this section of the road, and the first one coming in our direction threw a rock over our screen into our windshield. The smack of its impact jolted all of us, and the crack it left was three inches long.

"Oh, great," Tim said. "My poor car is taking a beating."

I felt bad for him. He was attached to his dependable workhorse. He'd started his painting business with it.

Five minutes later, another rock tossed from an oncoming truck put a smaller crack on the driver's side of the windshield.

"What's going on? Are we under attack?" Tim growled.

"Sure feels like it," Ben replied.

When a third rock smashed into the windshield a half hour later, Tim raged, "I'm pulling over. This is ridiculous!"

We all got out and checked the damage. The cracks were away from the driver's line of sight, but that didn't make Tim feel any better.

"There's nothing we can do about it anyway," Tim sighed. "But the windshield will have to be replaced eventually. At least the headlights are still working. But if this keeps up, there won't be much left of the car pretty soon."

We rumbled along in silence for an hour when Tim turned to me and yelled over the exhaust, "You smell gasoline?" he asked.

"Afraid so. Let's pull over and take a look."

Under the hood, we found the gas pump. At the gas line leaving it, we spotted the leak. Tim swiped it with his finger and took a whiff.

"That's it all right, but it doesn't look like it's leaking a lot," he said. "There's nothing dripping."

"It's coming from the flange nut connecting the line to the pump. Probably loose from all the vibration. Tightening that nut would probably fix it," I said, trying to lift his spirits.

"Yeah. And if it doesn't increase too fast, we can make it to a gas station in time," he said, sounding a bit more positive.

All this happened in a little over a 100 miles of gravel road. But there was more.

At the next gas station, in Talkeetna, we stopped for gas and got the flange nut tightened, which was a relief. We were intending to drive out the Kenai peninsula to Homer, where the road ends, and then retrace our route about 200 miles back to Anchorage, and from there, take the ferry down the Inside Passage to Seattle.

While paying for the gas I asked the attendant, "How often

does the ferry leave from Anchorage down the Inside Passage?"

"They're all booked until after Labor Day. Where are you trying to get to?"

"We were intending to sail through to Seattle," I said. "We're from the east coast. Is there a standby list?"

"Yes, but it's a mile long. The nearest spot to catch the ferry now is Haines. You might get a cancellation there."

"Do you mean Haines, south of Haines Junction? I asked.

"Exactly. It's a drive, for sure, but it's either that or sell your car in Anchorage and fly home," he replied.

"I don't think that would work for us, but thanks for your time," I said dejectedly.

"Sorry for the bad news. Good luck whatever you do."

"You, too," I said. Thanks for your help," I said.

Back at the car, I shared the news with my brothers.

"What do you mean no ferry from Anchorage? You sure about that?" Tim demanded.

"That's what the man said," I replied. We could check it with another source, but he seemed genuine to me," I said.

Ben said, "The car is taking a beating, so driving all those extra miles sure isn't going to help any."

"How many miles is it to Haines? Should we just skip the Kenai and go directly to Haines now?" Tim asked.

"Well, as best as I can figure it, it's about a thousand miles from Anchorage to Haines, and we're about a hundred and fifteen miles from Anchorage, which we have to go through no matter how we go. The trip down the peninsula from Anchorage to Homer and back is about four hundred and twenty–five miles. We could head to Haines from Anchorage and skip Homer, but there's good fishing out there," Ben replied, his voice flat.

"Shit," Tim said. "A thousand miles will take a toll on the Plymouth, especially on these roads. We can cover the window with plastic if we have to, but we don't know what else might happen."

"Not to mention the cost of the gas," I added.

Ben said, "We're getting about twenty-five miles a gallon, so a thousand miles is about forty gallons, or about twenty bucks in gas. We can afford that."

"I'm worried that the car will break down with the extra mileage," Tim said.

"It's your car, Tim, so it's your call," Ben replied. "Either way, we get it."

"Another option would be to sell the car and fly home, but I'm assuming that's not on the table," I added.

"I'm not selling the car," Tim said.

Trying to bring in some good news, I said, "We've come over six thousand miles without anything major going wrong with the car. For that matter, it could even break down between here and Anchorage, but I don't think it will. It's running great and not burning oil. And like you said, we can cover the window in plastic. But we'll have to stand the exhaust noise until we're forced to fix it. So, do we want to add the four hundred-plus miles to Homer or not?"

Just then, I looked up and saw a bald eagle perched in a tree so close I could almost count his feathers. Up until now, we'd seen only golden eagles, which are impressive for their slender tapers. This eagle was massive and broad-shouldered. Its white head and tail contrasted with its black body plumage and yellow talons, which clenched a poplar branch.

While we waited for Tim to decide, the eagle flicked its

head every so often in our direction, as if to let us know it was keeping track of us but in no way considered us a threat. Then it leapt from the limb, unfolded its wings, and for a second covered the sun. It was as if a silent airplane had just launched. With a few powerful strokes, it was over the ridge and out of sight. Then it occurred to me: bald eagles are fish–eating birds; the sight of this one might mean a plentiful food supply nearby.

"I'm going to ask the attendant about the fishing near here. Be right back," I said.

When I returned, Tim was lost in thought. Ben asked, "What'd he say?"

"He said the salmon are running in Sunshine Creek, which is between here and Anchorage, and not that far. He even told me what they've been getting them on," I said. "How about we fish now and decide on the peninsula after?"

"That sounds like a good idea," Tim said with relief.

Ben said, "Oh boy, salmon for dinner."

When we found, a few miles later, what we thought was the creek, it was running under the road, muddy with silt, and only about 15 feet wide. But there was a car and an old pickup parked just off the road and a path along the bank headed upstream. Without expecting anything, we got our rods and followed it.

Within about five minutes of walking, the creek bed opened into a clearing where the main stem split into two tributaries, one of which was carrying the mud and darkening the stream from here down. The other ran clear and stopped us in our tracks.

Pink salmon as long as your forearm emerged from the coffee–colored water of the main stem into the clear tributary in such numbers we stood transfixed. None of us had ever seen a school of any fish running up a freshwater river. There were hundreds of them, almost all about the same size, the same generation, born in this stream two years ago and now returning to spawn and die. They'd spent the intervening years in the rich waters of the Gulf of Alaska and the north Pacific feeding on the krill and shrimp that gave their flesh its pink color.

We didn't see any females preparing nests, which meant that they were headed even farther up one of the branches to lay their eggs. Those branches were only about 12 feet across. It was hard to imagine how even just the females, which were probably about half of what we saw, would have enough room in the small stream bed to lay anywhere between 1,000 and 2,000 eggs and still have room for the males to fertilize them. Those same females would then guard their nests until their death, which would come just days after spawning.

The wonder of such abundance clutched the root of my being. Often, when I looked into the rivers at home, and especially on opening day of trout season, I would imagine what it was like a mere 150 years ago, before the industrial revolution brought the dams that halted immense migrations of fish and the pollution that decimated their ranks. Who were we to do this in the name of progress and commerce? What gave us the right to deny these fish not just their lives, but their existence forever into the future?

We failed to realize that with their elimination we impoverished our own lives, despite what material benefits their destruction brought.

When I stood on the Saugatuck River bridge as a twelve-year–old and looked into the river below me, I saw the wild in my life and my life in the wild. The intimate connection to such a wild creature gave me a sense of belonging to this world. Trout reminded me viscerally that there were fellow creatures out there to help me avoid drowning in my family maelstrom. I needed their reminders that beauty arises from struggle, and that keen senses spring from active engagement of my total being. The kinship drew me to the stream, as if it was a part of me that I needed to stay in touch with. I felt honored by the company it offered.

On the Saugatuck, the river we knew best, posted signs told us we weren't welcome. To us, these signs were announcements that behind them the fishing was good. But it was more than just the lure of more and larger trout. To us, wandering the banks for miles, the river belonged to everyone. "Private property" and "river" didn't belong in the same category. We understood that people needed a spot on land. But the river was like the air or the stars to us. How do you claim the stars?

We were familiar with the idea of public property, but we didn't feel the same way about the Little League ball field as we did about the river. Adults had made the ball field for children to play in a controlled environment. Children had claimed the river for themselves, without adults, to explore an uncontrolled environment. That sense of ownership pushed us toward independence.

On the ball field, play unfolded predictably, with a winner and a loser. But the river bestowed surprises, even unwanted ones. When I stepped on a dinner plate–sized snapping turtle nestled in the mud, his thrashing threw me into the river. Yanking on a snagged lure, it recoiled at laser speed; it took me

20 minutes with my pocketknife to dig the treble hook out of my hand. When my bike broke miles from home, I had to fix it.

As kids, we knew this risk was the essence of adventure. Sometimes the adventures were funny and sometimes educational, full of wonder, or even frightening. Close calls were frequent, some even jeopardizing our safe return. And sometimes, in childish conviction or abandon, we'd do something stupid. We learned lessons that were either harsh reminders or confirmed our decisions. Either way, they formed our identities.

We were honest about our poaching. It raised the level of the stakes and the prizes. Sometimes I'd purposefully wander onto property where I wasn't sure what the reaction would be. This is easier to do if you're wading. You can claim you didn't see the signs, you're sorry, and so on. But I didn't own waders—my rod and tackle took every penny I had—so I tramped the bank and slid past the signs when I saw a tempting piece of water beyond them. Approaching irate landowners or their proxies gave me time to steel myself for their anger. Often, I was engrossed in casting, and suddenly they were standing behind me.

"Didn't you see the signs? This is posted property. You can't fish here." A question, a statement, a command, usually delivered with dismissal.

"Sorry, I must have missed them. Too busy I guess. I don't mean to bother anyone," I'd say, turning to face my evictor while reeling in.

"Well, you'd best be on your way now. I don't want to call the police. There's plenty of fish elsewhere."

"No problem. I'm on my way." To confirm my innocence, I'd

sometimes ask, "Could you tell me where this property ends? I want to be sure I'm fishing where it's okay."

"Beyond that sign is where this property ends," he'd say, pointing.

"Thank you," I'd say, walking off.

Tim was the Olympian in this endeavor, bold enough to sneak onto land owned and posted by a private fishing club, with a warden to patrol it. He was caught enough times to know the warden by name. The warden escorted him off the property each time until the last one, when he confiscated Tim's rod. His new one must have been a harsh reminder, but he still returned.

Sometimes I'd fish undisturbed, continuing my way downstream. Often, I'd find great spots as a result. I was always careful to tread lightly, leave no trace, and make no noise, figuring that if I wasn't bothering anyone, even though they might know I was there, they wouldn't take offense as long as I was behaving myself. But large, angry dogs, approaching rapidly, would send me sprinting for safe ground.

Sometimes I'd see signs and walk to the front door to ask for permission. Once, I knocked and an older woman opened the door.

"What do you want, young man?" she asked firmly.

"Well, ma'am, I was hoping you'd let me fish here. I saw the signs, but I promise to return all the fish I catch, unless of course you'd like some," I started. She looked at my torn jeans and soaked sneakers and I could see her resistance softening as I spoke. "And I'll be careful on your property," I continued, doing my best Huck Finn, asking a favor of the Widow Douglas.

"How long would you be?" she asked.

"I won't be long, I promise. Ten or fifteen minutes maybe,"

hoping she'd see me as harmless.

"Just for today?" she said, relaxing just a bit.

"Oh, yes, ma'am. I haven't fished here before and I'm curious. Would you like some fish if I catch any?" I asked, hoping to close the deal.

"No, thank you. That won't be necessary," she replied kindly, a hint of curiosity now showing in her eyes.

"Well perhaps I can get the mail from the mailbox or take out the trash?" I asked, willing to return a favor if I could.

"I'm all set for today. Maybe next time," she replied. And then she said what I was hoping for.

"You seem like a good boy. I suppose it would be all right to let you fish, if you're careful," she continued. "And be sure to come to the door, like you did today, if you return."

"Oh, yes, ma'am, I will. And thank you very much. You have a good day, and thanks again."

"You're welcome," she said, closing the door.

And whether the fishing turned out to be good or not, I'd ventured into unknown territory and achieved a goal for myself, by myself. I recognized that achievement for the precious item it was, and I always honored an owner's trust. Confidence is a gift you give yourself, but it's nurtured by those who trust you.

Many times I was caught on the river in a storm. I was usually alone, the fishing adults who might have been around having packed up and gone home. To be in the woods on such a blustery, downpour day made me feel alive. I was soaked through to my skin from the waist up, but I wasn't cold if I kept moving. Those were times I knew I would never have chosen to be out, but I was glad I was. My thoughts then were of how much longer I could fish, could be by this wonderful river before

I had to ride home. It didn't occur to me that I shouldn't be out there getting drenched. The river surrounded me with so much beauty, with such dynamic energy, that the world was at once a spectacle of natural wonder and a key to the center of life. I felt as though I was already home.

Chapter 20

At our camp on Sunshine Creek, we caught lots of salmon of about four pounds but kept only the two we knew we could eat. We camped along the road next to a tremendous pile of scrap wood, which both grilled our fish and kept us warm. After a few sumptuous meals of all the salmon we could eat, a kind woman we met at the creek told us about the equally fabulous crabbing and clamming on the coast at Homer, and we decided to try it out, despite the extra mileage we'd put on the car. To get there, we'd have to drive through Anchorage.

After the drive south with the still roaring muffler, cracked windshield, and broken window crank, we thought Anchorage would bring relief. But the sudden stimulation of a city after a long removal from it can be so great as to unhinge your mental functioning. After weeks of seeing only trees, rivers, fish, and animals, now seeing the world of people, with the noise, traffic, and buildings, came as an alarming shock. We succumbed to this onslaught and, after a meal in a restaurant and showers at the Russian Jack Camp Ground, we sampled the bars and liquor stores.

We woke up with headaches to the sound of a garbage truck compacting its load and found a laundromat. Our clothes hadn't been cleaned since Banff, and the rinse water ran black.

We also confirmed the fact that the ferry was booked until after Labor Day, which also established our need to drive the additional 1,000 miles to Haines. And there was no guarantee of a ferry ride even there. Ben might be late returning to school. But we were here and wanted to see Homer, a town out on the Kenai Peninsula known for the world's longest spit, a four and a half-mile finger of land that juts out into Kachemak Bay. So we piled in and drove further south.

Clam Gulch, a small town on the way to Homer, sounded and looked like a great place to try some clamming, but we were informed that the special low tide needed for that wasn't due for another two weeks. So we walked the beach with eyes on the water for seals and orcas. Next to a trailer set into the base of a gravel bank, we spotted a wooden crate about the size of a small car, mounded with freshly caught salmon. The trailer owner emerged, and, in our chat, described his life on that beach where he returned each summer from California, to net the returning salmon. Poking around in the crate, he pulled out a fish he was proud of. "This king will go about thirty-five pounds," he said. Perhaps four feet long, the eye gazed at us above a gill the size of a coffee saucer. This one, and its brethren, were headed for the cannery within a few hours. There was an exposed coal seam in the bank behind the trailer, from which he plucked chunks of shiny black anthracite to warm the trailer during the cold and rainy summers. He tended his gill net, stretching out from the beach, with an outboard skiff he beached next to the net's anchor onshore.

In September, he returns to California, when his girls start school. Gravity-fed freshwater arrived in a pipe from a spring on the hillside above, and a constantly spinning wind prop on the roof provided electricity for a small refrigerator and lights. The kitchen was complete with a gas stove. All of this required less than a day to set up upon his arrival in June and the same time to break down, store, and secure when he and his family left, nearly three months later. He hauled his nets by hand twice each day, a job that took him only an hour. The remainder of the day was his. Here was a man in control of his life, living honestly and productively fulfilled. It was the sense of self-reliance and balance that I wanted.

The next day we counted our money: 650 dollars. We'd driven 6,500 miles on nearly 200 dollars worth of gasoline. With close to that much in gas costs for the return and a ferry ticket (if we could buy one) of about 250 dollars, we were approaching our turnaround point. Homer, the last town you could get to by car on the Kenai, was just up the road by Alaskan standards, and a timely and natural pivot point.

The harbor in Homer is tucked into the protected side of the spit, one branch of which extends over two miles into Kachemak Bay. We drove to the end and found the commercial fishing boats. Crewmen were unloading their shrimp catch, and Ben asked if he could buy some. What one crewman did next surprised us.

With the oversized aluminum grain shovel he was using to funnel the shrimp being hoisted from the hold into large bins, he scooped a huge pile into a plastic bag, which another crewman held open. This second fellow swung the bag up onto the dock at our feet and said, "Will that do?" Slack-jawed, we were gaping at over ten pounds of shrimp.

"Yeah, I'm sure," Ben stammered, then asked in return, "How much do we owe you?" "You can have those," came the reply. Awed once again by the generosity of complete strangers, we thanked the crew profusely. They looked at us with grinning faces, and in that glow I saw volumes of good will. We hefted our bag and strode down the dock, towards shore.

"Do you believe that?" Ben asked.

"These people are as large as the land," I replied. Then I added, "Now all we have to do is clean them."

An hour later, with all three of us working at it, we had two piles: one of cleaned shrimp and one of shells and heads. We took the cleaned pile and found a seafood shop, where they cooked our treasure, along with the dozens of other batches they were boiling, and handed them back to us within a few minutes. As I opened my wallet, the cook looked at me and said, "Just give me thirty cents." Ben went next door to the Land's End Café and brought back three coffees and a bottle of cocktail sauce. For less than two dollars, all three of us gorged on shrimp and washed them down with java. It was wonderful to enjoy a meal that wasn't peanut butter, sardines, or oatmeal with the obligatory Tang.

Conscious of our low funds and spurred by our success at rustling a delicious but inexpensive meal, we decided to press our luck and apply for jobs at the cannery that the friendly waitress at the café had told us was hiring. Tim and I walked to the building hanging over the water a bit farther down the dock and asked our way to the boss.

We were directed to a muscular, middle–aged man with winter in his hair who was dressed in the oilskin apron that everyone was wearing.

"We understand you're hiring workers and we'd like to apply for whatever jobs we're suited for," Tim explained after the opening introductions.

"Right now," he said, "the king crabs are still coming strong, so we're busy with them and have enough help. But that can change overnight and probably will soon because their run is approaching the end of its normal length. Why don't you stop by tomorrow evening? We'll have a better idea then of when we'll need more help. Oh, and just to let you know, you'll have to shave. Health regulations require it."

"No problem with that," Tim replied. "And thanks. We'll return tomorrow to talk with you again."

Walking back to our campground on the beach, I said, "I sure hope we can get those jobs. The extra money would give us a cushion for the ride home and might even allow us to repair the car. It's looking pretty sad."

We were all sick of the exhaust's racket and the driver's window, which had to be manually lifted and only when the car was stopped. There was a cluster of new cracks in the windshield, some of which seemed to be growing, and there were dings in the panels behind the rear wheels. Our flagship, having faithfully borne us to the land of our dreams, deserved attention. And that was just the outside.

Weeks of accumulated road dirt, dropped from our boot treads, covered the floor, both front and back. The windows were grimy from our constant smoking. The ashtray overflowed with our hand-rolled cigarette butts, and the rear seat was mounded with debris—clothes, boxes of crackers, peanut butter jars, maps, and sleeping bags. All found their way to the back seat because, in the constant rain along the coast, it was the only place that our belongings would have a chance to dry. They weren't drying too well, either, although occasionally we'd start the car and blast the heater in a futile attempt to drive some moisture from the pile. Fortunately, the car was still starting easily and the engine was running smoothly, despite the exhaust racket. Even the rubber plug the mechanic back in Val D'Or, Quebec, had installed was still in place, and the tire looked fine. We checked the oil level frequently, and the engine wasn't burning a drop.

A thorough car cleaning was in order as soon as the rain stopped, and my thoughts were drifting to this when the crest of what looked like an abnormally big wave, just offshore, caught my eye. Then another, smaller wave, rose in front of the first. A fountain of spray erupted right behind it, the torso of an enormous creature took form underneath it, and in awe we realized we were watching an orca hunting a seal. All our eyes were fixed on the unfolding scene as predator and prey moved swiftly up the shore through the mist-enshrouded rollers. The killer whale, close to 30 feet long and as big around as our car, rose from the water in incredible lunges and closed the gap. It was difficult to believe. Something that big shouldn't be moving that fast. The seal sounded, perhaps seeking shelter underwater, and the orca followed; just like that, the surface resumed its regular appearance.

"I'm pulling for the seal," I said.

In unison, Tim and Ben responded, "So am I."

When we returned to the car, we tackled the clean-up despite the continuing rain, which we now realized was always going to be with us. It was both a fact of life and, as we thought of the seal, of death. "The sun shines," as John Muir said, "not on us, but in us." Hitching your outlook or your plans to the weather was pointless.

So, even though (or maybe because) it was still raining the next morning, we rose early, fixed a hot breakfast of oatmeal and coffee, and drove to the Anchor River, about 20 miles north on the coast road. Tim was out of the car and casting before I had even strung up my rod. By the time I had and walked to the bank, he was battling a salmon that both of us knew right away was too big for his tackle. He'd pull to the line's breaking point and couldn't budge the fish. Then the fish would calmly move farther off, easily pulling line from the reel, and settle into a new spot. Tim would pump, tug, and haul with the same result. The salmon, so large as to not be affected in the least by an eight–pound test connection to an increasingly frustrated Tim, refused to even acknowledge the encounter. Tim had fished much more in the ocean than I had and had hooked large, reluctant striped bass before. But, after balking at first, they had eventually engaged. He'd even caught some of them.

A half hour later, this situation was still a standoff. The fish hadn't given an inch. He was still solidly hooked, a fact we could all easily see from our spot on the bank, and something Ben and I could also see was beginning to frustrate Tim. Still, being hooked to this monster was good; having the fish in charge wasn't. Here was the issue of fair play, displayed with an ironic twist. With the roles reversed, the question became, will the fish give the angler a sporting chance? After half an hour of suspended resolution, Tim decided he wouldn't wait any longer for an answer. He had done his part by hooking the fish. Now it was the salmon's turn to fulfill his role by putting up a fight. If he wasn't going to do that, then Tim would take the fight to the fish.

"Going to be stubborn, are you? We'll see about that," Tim muttered, plunging into the current towards the salmon and reeling slack wildly. He'd gotten about to his hips when the salmon, sitting at the tail of the pool and aware that something was up, casually turned downstream into the current, calmly heading for the ocean. Tim stopped where he was and watched as line stripped from the spool, the drag now clicking wildly. Before the salmon emptied the reel, there was only one choice.

Tim tightened the tension on the drag all the way, leaned back on the rod with both hands and turned his head away from the fish, in case the lure, bristling with treble hooks, suddenly released and came flying back at him. Ben and I cringed as we watched the bending rod double over. The line from the rod tip drew a laser straight to the fish far downstream. The next second, the lure released, and Tim, unable to catch his balance, fell backward and went under, rod in hands, as the three-inch metal spoon, loaded with hooks, strafed the water's surface coming full bore back upstream, thankfully missing Tim. Ben and I started laughing so hard our stomachs hurt and were still out of control as Tim slogged his way up the bank, water pouring off him everywhere.

"Well, at least he returned my lure," he spluttered. "Maybe he thought he was just renting it."

This, as it turned out, was what we were all to experience on the Anchor River that day. Sometimes we lost the lure, and sometimes yards of line with it, when the fish we hooked departed for preferred locations. And we frequently hooked fish, so the script was almost always being acted out by one of us. Sometimes, two of us had fish on at the same time. The salmon played their parts unflinchingly, sometimes even moving after being hooked, though not, of course, in response to anything we did. They might glide upstream or down in complete oblivion to any attachment, as we pirouetted on the bank in response, ducking under lines to prevent tangling.

Once, Tim and Ben even hooked the same salmon with another angler up the bank and with three lines joined, coordination of the fishermen onshore verged on traffic control. Within half an hour, the salmon had broken all three lines. As the afternoon unfolded, the Anchor River became the angler's version of purgatory, a fishing mecca where you were doomed to hook a salmon on every cast but never land it. As dinnertime approached and our tackle box emptied, we packed up and headed home. The Knights of the Creel, having found the sacred piscatorial sword in the stone, had not been able to remove it.

Chapter 21

Back in Homer, we checked on the cannery jobs, but were told the king crabs were still strong. The wait would be longer than we could bear. Our journey's turning point stepped forward to claim priority, and with our dwindling funds in mind we had our last pie and coffee at the Land's End Café and said our goodbyes.

We were back on the road, and the road's grinding annoyances returned. The driver's window rattled, the exhaust droned underneath us, and the cracks crawled toward the center of the windshield. The rain hadn't stopped since we'd come from Anchorage days ago. But the largest black cloud in the brewing thunderstorm of our temperament was the slowly descending reality that, without ferry passage, we were most likely going to have to drive all the way back down the AlCan. The latest hope we had was that we might be able to board on a standby basis. We were waiting for a no-show or a cancellation and were intending to find out if such plans had any chance.

The climate in the car mirrored the steel-gray cloud cover, and the steady rain pelted the forest. On we droned, all voices silent, lost in brooding thought. Verbal exchanges, when there were any, were sharp and coarse. Returning to dirt road, after a brief section of pavement on the Kenai, slowed our pace and darkened our outlook.

After five hours of this building storm, as we approached Anchorage, Tim muttered out of the blue, "I'm going to find a repair shop. I need to get the exhaust fixed."

"Okay with me," I replied.

"Me too," Ben added.

When we arrived in Anchorage we drove to five repair shops, all closed. The edge in our voices increased. It was after five p.m. when we pulled into the sixth closed shop. Tim said, "Okay, guys. What do you want to do now?"

"I'd like to get this exhaust pipe silenced," I said, and then continued, "If we've got to drive back down the AlCan, we're going to have to get that fixed to preserve our sanity."

Tim's frustration flared. "Well, sure. But we've now driven to six repair shops that were closed. Got any other bright ideas?" I looked at Ben's grim face to see if he'd heard the provocation that I'd heard. If he did, his expression wasn't giving it away.

Trying to lower the tension, I offered a plan. "Well, this is the largest town we'll see until we get to Dawson Creek, if we have to go that way, and it's our best chance for finding a good repair. We've already tried a patch weld and that didn't work. I say we look around some more and maybe even spend the night if we have to get the repair done in the morning."

"That's crazy," Tim challenged. "I'm not spending the night. We're running out of money and we've got to keep going or we're not going to make it home." Looking for an ally, he finished, "What do you think, Ben?"

Trying to find middle ground, Ben said, "I'd like to keep going also. I'm the one who's got to make it home in time for school. But our chances for making it back at all may be zero if we don't maintain the car. I'd hate to have to abandon the car and take a bus home. We owe ourselves, and this car, more than that."

Tim yelled, "What if we have to abandon the car or sell it because we've spent so much of our money on repairs that we don't have enough to get home? What would you suggest then? This is *my* car and I'm damn sure I don't want to sell it out here and have no car when I get back!"

"We'll have to cross that bridge when we come to it. If we got a repair now, we'd also be reducing the risk of breaking down miles from nowhere and having to pay for a very expensive tow job on top of the repair. At least we should get an estimate," I replied.

"I'm not waiting!" Tim announced. "I'm driving to the airport and catching the next flight to New York. I've had enough of this!"

With that, he jammed the car into drive and screeched into the street, headed for the airport. Ben and I exchanged tense looks. We drove in silence to the airport. Tim pulled in, found a parking spot, and brought the car to an abrupt stop. Slamming his door as he got out, he muttered, "See you guys later," and started marching for the terminal.

I jumped out and raced after him yelling, "Tim! You can't do this! This is our trip together and if you leave now, you'll ruin that. Look, there's a lot of great wilderness left on our way back home in the parks out west and plenty of good fishing, all of which we'll miss exploring together." When I caught up to him, I grabbed the sleeve of his sweatshirt to slow him down. In response, he grabbed two fistfuls of sweatshirt on my chest and shoved me away.

"I'm doing this, Buck! Don't get in my way!"

"Okay, Tim. But you're wrecking it. And you don't have to. We can find a solution that will work for all of us." But I was talking to his departing back now, and to the rain. Soaked, I slogged back to the car, where Ben was sitting in the rear seat.

"What do we do now, bro?" he asked as I got in.

"I don't know, Ben. Let's just wait here for now. I'm in no hurry to go anywhere just this second."

The rain plinked on the roof, spattered on the windshield, and ran in rivulets down the windows. Steam rose off the hood and thunder rumbled in the distance. In the back, Ben rolled a cigarette and smoked it. Ben was always good at waiting, surrounded as he had been by crazy adults most of his life. It had become a default strategy and a sensible one, given that he'd been at the mercy of those same adults whenever family life erupted.

Tim and I, on the other hand, being older and able to, ran. Through the door, into the woods, away from the insanity. Flight was also rewarding because it was immediate. Eventually, we'd return home, but running provided relief and a temporary illusion that we could improve our situation through action. Doing something preserved the sense that we had some control over our lives. But standing still had its advantages, and Ben, too small to run with us, had found them. Primary among them was that in running you could worsen your situation, but by waiting, you rarely did. Wait and see now served us both.

I was just about to start the engine when I saw Tim weaving through the parking lot, looking up in the rain now and then to get a fix on the car.

When he got in, all he said was, "All outbound flights have

been delayed indefinitely due to the weather. Let's just keep going."

I started the car, eased out of the parking lot, and found the road toward Glennallen, a mere 200 miles northeast. No one said anything. The crisis had passed, but we still hadn't solved our problem, a situation the once again roaring exhaust reminded us of.

We made it through the fog and rain to Glennallen, arriving about 11 p.m. After fueling, we continued north for another 125 miles to Tok, where we gassed up again. From Tok it was 300 miles south to Haines Junction, where we'd have a decision to make.

From Haines Junction, we could play the safe but longer–by–far choice east toward Whitehorse and retrace our route back down the AlCan. Or, from Haines Junction, we could continue south for 150 miles, dead–ending at Haines. If we caught a ferry there, we could save ourselves about 950 miles of driving. If we didn't, with the round trip back up to Haines Junction, we'd have added another 300 miles to that 950. We drove all night and got to Haines Junction about ten in the morning. We'd driven for 17 hours straight, over 600 miles on dirt roads.

The driving had us all punchy, so the decision to take our chances on ferry passage was more of a stumble in the direction we'd been going than a conscious choice. Anything that might help us avoid the monotony of driving seemed like a good idea, even if it was a long shot. We needed a change from sitting in the car, subjected to the constant roar of the unmuffled V–8. And the sheer distances were catching up with us. There had been too much driving with not enough tramping since the Anchor River, which now seemed months ago.

So it was no surprise that I found myself behind the wheel of the bellowing Plymouth about 100 miles south of Haines Junction with still another 50 to Haines. But it was a surprise when the sun suddenly burst through and had me squinting at the dirt road in front of me through the glistening brilliance of the wet, shimmering forest.

I was so focused on staying on the winding road that I didn't notice the white Ford Maverick until it was right along side me, mirrors nearly touching, a shock so sudden I nearly veered off the road. Between my swerve and the Maverick, which was fishtailing wildly as it passed us on a blind curve, my brothers were fully alert and temporarily stunned. Stones blasted from his spinning rear tires, clattered and pinged off our doors and grill. The roar of the barrage even drowned out our rattling exhaust. He was drifting sideways as much as he was going straight and even though I'd slowed, it was still taking him a long time to pass us. It was long enough to wonder, for an uncomfortably long time, what might be coming around the corner just ahead.

"What's this guy doing!" yelled Ben.

"He's going to get us all killed!" shouted Tim, above the din.

I braked hard, and launched both of them into bracing themselves on whatever was in front of them, but not so hard as to cause us to skid. The Maverick, even after passing us, continued to veer insanely from one side of the road to the other as it disappeared around the corner. We all got out to inspect the Plymouth. There were a few new dents and scratches as well as a new nick in the windshield, but otherwise it seemed okay. We, on the other hand, were still shaking. We paced nervously around the car, working off our scare.

"What was wrong with that guy?" Ben asked.

"Seemed like he was on something," I mumbled, my hands still quivering. "What he did was insane."

"We should report him when we get to Haines," Tim suggested. And then he added, "If he gets there."

"Someone else want to drive?" I asked. "I could use a break."

"Sure. I'll take over," Tim said. "We've only got another fifty miles to Haines."

"Seems funny hearing you say that 'only fifty miles,' Tim. But I guess it shows what distances we've gotten used to up here. Anything less than triple digits is just a trip to the store," Ben remarked.

All of a sudden it occurred to me that Ben hadn't driven since our brush with the Mounties in Saskatchewan and I wondered how he felt about returning to his role as a passenger. Was he relieved or did he miss the excitement?

"How about you, Ben? You haven't driven in a while," I said.

"Not right now, thanks," Ben replied. "That guy scared me, and I'm still new to driving. But I'd be glad to make us all some peanut butter and jelly sandwiches. Right now, I'm pretty hungry."

"Thanks, Ben. I'm ravenous too."

Back in the Belvedere, we rolled down all the windows, passed out sandwiches and fruit, and the Plymouth rumbled southward under the shining sun.

About ten minutes into our ride, with some relaxation returning, we rounded a curve and the white Maverick was on the side of the road, on its roof, the still spinning tires pointed at the sky. The driver was walking in circles around the car, staring at the ground. We pulled over and approached cautiously, afraid of what we didn't want to see.

The driver, a thin, young man, was standing near the steaming car, mumbling to himself, and didn't acknowledge us. We waited, thinking he would eventually calm down and talk to us.

His car was a shocking sight. The roof had been crushed to the door line on the passenger's side from the force of the roll. All the glass was shattered, some of it gone, and the engine's fluids were gurgling and whooshing. Metal everywhere ticked as it cooled.

The man had crawled out through the driver's window. I walked toward him, surprised he wasn't injured, and asked him, "Are you all right, sir?"

His response was so incoherent we had no idea what he was saying. We were only able to decipher his speech because he repeated what he'd said and kept repeating it.

What finally emerged from his garbles was, "I am Danny Franklin and I'm okay." He repeated what he'd said and kept repeating this rote sentence in a monotone, as if his mind had caught on a track and kept skipping. He seemed neither aware nor unaware of what he was repeating, but also seemed compelled to continue. We offered him a ride to Haines and even though he didn't respond, we guided him toward the back seat of the Plymouth, explaining to him as clearly as we could that we were taking him to Haines, where he could arrange to have his car towed and find help for himself.

He replied to none of what we were saying, but allowed us to lead him gently to our car. Ben, Tim, and I all looked nervously at each other, knowing the question each of us was asking: "Should we do this?"

But there was no choice. We had no way to contact either the police or an ambulance, and the nearest help, whatever it might be, was now about 40 miles away, in Haines. Not to mention the fact that this man was in no shape to be making decisions for himself. He was in shock, that much was obvious, and had probably sustained a severe concussion and may even have been bleeding internally. I looked back at his car as I eased him into ours and realized that it was a miracle he was alive. But there was nothing we could do that would improve his condition and certainly nothing we could do to repair his car. He needed the attention of someone who could provide more help than we could, both for himself and his car.

On the way to Haines, Danny stopped mumbling and, in fact, stopped talking altogether. We thought he might be calming down but were also worried he might be losing his ability to speak. He'd nod when we asked him if he was all right and then resume staring out the window. We were speaking openly about him, and questions of where to take him in Haines came up.

"Let's see if there's a garage where he can have his car towed and repaired, if that's possible," Tim suggested.

"I think he needs medical attention, guys," Ben said. "It's amazing he's not seriously injured, but he's acting odd and should be seen by a doctor."

Ben was right, but that wasn't registering with either Tim or me because when we drove into Haines, one of the first places we saw was Wallace's Garage, and we pulled in. We helped Danny out, escorted him to the mechanic and began explaining the situation. Danny jumped in and delivered the story in droning repetition, and we could see the mechanic squinting with the effort to understand. Between us, the events were eventually clarified, and the mechanic agreed to retrieve Danny's car with his wrecker. He and Danny were making arrangements for this, and Danny seemed able to handle himself. We watched them for a while and then, sensing we were no longer needed, began to withdraw.

"Good luck," I said. "We're very glad you aren't hurt any worse. Please find a doctor and have him check you over. You had a terrible accident and are very lucky."

"Yes, get a checkup soon. Take care of yourself," Ben added.

"Glad we could help," Tim said. "Best of luck."

No one mentioned the car.

For the first time, Danny looked us in the eye. "Thank you. Thank you very much," he replied, extending his hand for a shake. As we left, we were relieved that Danny had recovered enough to help himself somewhat. I was hoping he'd continue to improve.

We drove to the harbor and found a campground right on the shore, where we claimed a site that had a small roofed woodshed on it. We spread belongings out to dry and then headed to the ferry office to find out if our gamble was going to pay off. It started to rain again, which I took as a bad omen.

When we told the ticket agent we'd like to book passage to Seattle, she said there were no vacancies for the foreseeable future. It didn't matter anyway, because the fare she quoted was over 300 dollars, more than we could afford and still have enough to make it home. The next option was passage to Prince Rupert, British Columbia, which, at a mere 234 dollars, was half of our remaining funds, but it still cut off 950 miles of driving. The ride would take three days. We booked it, glad our gamble had paid off. It would leave in two days, time we'd have to enjoy Haines in the rain.

At our camp, we had the woodshed roof to help us stay dry, though the rain prevented a wood fire. The car's heater would have been a welcome source of warmth in the rain, but now the starter wasn't always working and we'd had to get the car jump–started to drive from the garage to the harbor. We were pretty sure that with the cash we had left, getting it fixed would leave us short for the return. As it was, we'd be sleeping on the ship's deck in lounge chairs because we couldn't afford a cabin and sleeping in your vehicle below, in the hold, wasn't allowed. Taking a chance that the starter would work when we needed it made sense. Or seemed to.

Chapter 22

With the constant rain at the campsite and a sharp eye on our expenses, without discussion we decided to stay put and find diversions to occupy our wait. Being at the end of the only road, 146 miles back to Haines Junction, we didn't have anywhere to go by land. The intermittent function of the car's starter made driving anywhere risky, and we were hoping to conserve what strength it had to get us on the ferry. Many, if not all, of our fellow campers were also biding time until their ferries departed. Hikes were possible, but in the constant rain they offered no views and the certainty of getting soaked. We had a back seat full of wet clothing already and were struggling to dry that out.

I tried fishing from shore, walking to a spot away from the ferry dock and town, but my heart wasn't in it. The rain soaked me through my raincoat, the ocean seemed too big for my puny spinning rod and undersized tackle, and I was clueless about saltwater angling. But it was fishing, what I'd come to do. I was completely shocked when, after what seemed like futile hours in the rain, I caught a small cod. The occasion prompted my first smile in days.

One of the benefits of having the Tongass National Forest all around us were the bald eagles that gathered in the tall conifers between the campground and the water. We were astonished at their numbers, saw scores of them day after day. I tried to tally just the ones I could see from the woodshed and stopped counting at 168.

The Tongass is home to the largest breeding density of bald eagles in the world. They were all big and some of them were huge, three feet tall with a wingspan equal to the height of a typical doorway. We'd look up from the woodshed and see eagles soaring over the water, cruising the shoreline for prey, or actually plunging into the water for it. Some were landing, others were perched, some preening, others launching. They had all come for the fish.

Their nests, which adorned the giant spruces, were perched mostly near the treetops, but could also be found lower down, wherever an opening allowed them to land. There were plenty of ospreys too, also focused on the fish, and also more successful than the eagles. When an osprey held a fish, the eagles would often steal that fish right from its talons or harass it until the osprey finally dropped it, like school cafeteria bullies shaking down a smaller kid for lunch money. And yet, as huge as they were, the eagles were cowards; when attacked boldly by a tiny king bird, they turned and flew away.

I was reminded of our own thieving—how blind we'd been to consideration for others, to our own selfish behavior, to how close we'd come to serious consequences. We'd been lucky, and after Jasper, we realized it and suspended our game. We hadn't lifted even a sugar packet since then. We weren't on the open road as much as at the dead end of it, with nowhere to run should we get caught. But with our money running out and our patience shrinking in the rain, the temptation was rising.

We focused on making warm meals under the shelter, playing chess, and reading. When I'd finished every book and magazine we had, I walked into town and bought a used paperback. I spotted Danny Franklin, the Maverick driver, on the other side of the street, and crossed to say hello.

"Hi, Danny. How are you?" I asked him.

"Hello," he replied cautiously. It was obvious by his look that he didn't recognize me.

"How are you feeling? Did you see a doctor?" I asked.

"Okay, okay," he said. But he looked as though he was somewhere else.

I'd seen his car at Wallace's garage, looking even worse than I remembered, and I asked him, "How's your car? Were they able to repair it?"

"The car is fine. The car is fine," he said, continuing to stare blankly at me.

And that was all. No "Thank you for the ride" or "How are you?" It was clear that although he thought his car was fine, he himself wasn't. When I asked him what he was planning to do, the question didn't register. "I'm fine," he said, and then repeated, "I'm fine," with his uncomfortable stare.

"Well, take care of yourself, and good luck," I replied. And with that he walked away. I watched him drift off, eventually turning a corner. All the way back to the campsite, I worried about Danny. He was lost, off somewhere, impossible to reach.

In a certain sense, even though I had a grasp of current reality, I was the same myself. Drifting, unmoored, aimlessly expending energy trying to find my anchor. This trip was an attempt, tramping the continent, the wilderness, to find something that would transform me, the nature of which was totally unknown to me, to help me make the passage into the next phase of my life. I had no response to the big "now what?" question my life posed.

I kept looking at what most of us, by habit or training, look at: those things that are measurable, practical, concrete. They were the benchmarks against which I'd gauged my progress: grades in school, holding a job, graduation. They were the things known to me, things that can be measured. But in our world what can be measured almost always takes precedence over what cannot. We value the quantifiable, with its speed and efficiency, over enjoyment and quality, over the mysteries and meanings in life that hold more importance for fully living, but cannot be measured. It was the immeasurable, the unknown to me, that I needed to find. How could I stretch myself into new ground and experiment with becoming someone else?

I'd been reading Timothy Leary, the dropped-out Harvard professor, cum counterculture guru, who'd been urging his readers to "be here now." To be fully immersed in the present is to be open to uncertainty, things that cannot be measured or counted, only anticipated. To plan for the unknown requires valuing its importance, remaining open, even embracing chance and surprise, and accepting that there are some essential mysteries in the world and thereby a limit to our efforts to control.

Using a system that ignores the mystery of what cannot be counted contributes to the destruction of the earth because it can't count what matters. When we awaken our imaginations to the unknown, to what matters, we reject this destruction in favor of pleasures money can't buy and corporations can't direct, in favor of being producers rather than consumers of meaning, in favor of the slow, the meandering, the exploratory, the spiritual, the uncertain.

From where I was standing, though, the slow and meandering rivulets of rainwater were slithering down my back and legs and filling my boots; the monotonous certainty of the rain held us all in its grip, and the uncertainty of even getting the car started seemed as deep as the cloud bank overhead. The rain itself seemed both more depressing and irrelevant.

Chapter 23

No matter what I thought about the rain, however, which had fallen now for ten days straight, it was the reason that southeast Alaska comprises the largest remaining temperate rain forest in the world. Running from Yakutat in the north to below Ketchikan in the south, the Tongass National Forest, at 17 million acres, about 26,500 square miles, includes almost all of southeast Alaska. The Tongass itself is over three times the size of the next largest national forest. In fact, it's larger than nine U.S. states and several entire nations and contains nearly a third of the old–growth temperate rain forest in the world.

The highest coastal range in the world separates the more than 5,000 islands of the Alexander Archipelago from interior Canada. As a barrier, the Coast Mountains block incoming weather, and storms drop up to 200 inches of rain a year. The Tongass is also topped by one of the largest ice masses in North America; the Malaspina Glacier is larger than Rhode Island. All this water, from snow pack runoff, glacier melt, and rain, creates 4,500 salmon spawning streams, to which the 50 to 60 million salmon spawn every year. The salmon support not only the eagles, but also the bears and, in fact, the trees.

The migration of salmon brings energy in sequential surges over the course of the different runs throughout the year. The fish bring protein, fat, nitrogen, and phosphorus, as super concentrated nutrients, into the interior, sometimes as much as 1,000 miles from the ocean. Their prolific runs support dense populations of bears. At 1,700 square miles, Admiralty Island is home to 1,700 bears, one of the highest densities in the world. Another island, Kuiu, supports the densest population of black bears ever surveyed. Altogether, southeast Alaska harbors 80 bears for every *one* that lives in areas far from salmon streams.

Researchers say a bear may carry 40 salmon from a stream in eight hours, leaving a couple hundred pounds of concentrated nutrients on the forest floor. In some streams, bears carry more than half the salmon into the forest. So many salmon, in fact, that the concentration of nitrogen and phosphorus near some Alaskan streams exceeds recommended concentrations for commercial fertilizer. Up to 70 percent of the nitrogen in streamside foliage originates in the ocean, brought by salmon, delivered by bears, drawn into the roots of plants.

Not only do the salmon grow forests; the forests also grow salmon. Because of the storage capacity of the mossy rain forest floor, streams flow more evenly and more dependably for the salmon. Fallen trees create pools and eddies that break the current, providing rest and shelter to small fish. These same log structures protect the juveniles from getting swept seaward when currents flow hard with the surge of flooding rains. Salmon are here, to an extent, because of the trees.

In winter, the canopy of the great conifers carries the snow, preventing too much from accumulating on the forest floor and covering the forage available to animals. And just as they moderate the temperature and snow depth on the forest floor, the great overhanging branches also protect the water from freezing extremes. In the summer, shade helps stabilize and cool stream temperatures. Huddled as the three of us were under those same great limbs, they were also sheltering us from rain that, unchecked, would have had us soaked constantly. And like the salmon and the trees, we were dependent upon each other.

Finally, our departure day arrived. We spent the morning cleaning, arranging, and packing the car, and making sure it would start with repeated practice starts. When it was time, it did, and, with a sigh of relief we drove to the ferry dock and got in line with a noisy invasion of vehicles.

Passenger cars, RVs, (some towing cars), cars with trailers, construction vehicles, some also towing trailers with heavy equipment, buses, and tractor trailers jockeyed for position. We filed down a spiral ramp to the vehicle deck, a ballfield–sized cavern, clamoring with the echoes of vehicle engines and the ship's engine room racket. With all the distractions, I wasn't following the attendant's waving arms closely enough, because when I thought I had, he slammed both of his hands on the hood and yelled, "Bring it over more!" After I had, we crawled out the windows because there wasn't room enough to open the doors.

To get a fix on finding our car later, I scanned the floor for a relative position. Toward the closest wall, there were five cars ahead of us and ten cars behind us, although I couldn't be sure, with tractor–trailers and buses obstructing my view. The rows seemed about a dozen across but there were blocks to my view in that direction also. The rough math gave me an estimate of somewhere over 150 vehicles packed below the water line. With the spread so vast, I wondered how we'd find our vehicle when we had to.

We climbed flights of stairs to the main deck, where Ben

and Tim found the ping-pong table and I read. The steel-gray water of Lynn Canal parted as we cast off about 5:30 p.m., heading south. The rain had finally stopped, although the cloud cover lingered. At least the long chairs, where we'd be sleeping that night, were drying out. Peanut butter and jelly sandwiches, washed down with Tang, made a passable dinner, although I was conscious of other passengers watching us eat, camping, as it were, amongst the deck furniture. The cafeteria inside, cozy and warm, was beyond our budget. For dessert, we decided to explore the ship. There were some cabin levels below, as well as the kitchen, which drew our attention with its commotion and aromas.

The MV Wickersham, only five years old, was a state ferry, so accommodations were basic. We peeked into an open cabin to discover that it was merely a bunkroom, and a cramped one at that, without a sink or a toilet. There weren't enough cabin beds for all the passengers, so we knew there'd be others sleeping on the furniture, either outside like us, or inside, in what was generously referred to as the lounge but which looked more like the waiting room at a large bus depot. We found long chairs outside under a roof, and staked them out with our backpacks, counting ourselves lucky.

The ship docked in Juneau around 12:30 a.m. under a clearing sky, which, given the latitude, was still more like dusk than midnight. The announcement came that we had two hours to go ashore and return, so we headed out to see the state capital, the only one you can't drive to. With only about 15,000 residents, it was still the second largest city by area in the U.S., over 3,200 square miles, larger than Rhode Island. Its eastern edge borders Canada.

To our surprise, bars, restaurants, souvenir shops, and theaters on the main street were open and busy. The city sits below mountains so steep no roads traverse them, and in the moonlight we could see the two glaciers, Mendenhall and Lemon Creek, that flow from the ice field above. Despite the hour, we were able to buy a large bottle of wine before returning to the ship.

Still excited from our city lights exposure and glad to be moving again, we uncorked the bottle and unpacked our tin cups. Our conversation centered on the promise of more great fishing to come: streams in British Columbia where we'd be landing, and the fabled waters of Yellowstone and the Tetons. The rivers were unlimited and our plans were big and got bigger the more we drank. No one thought to count our money.

By the time the bottle was nearly gone, we'd exhausted our fishing plans and were hungry for the dessert we missed. I was headed for the kitchen before I knew it, but long before I got there I could smell the pies. As I turned the corner, they appeared in a row, like toys lined up for a parade. The cook had laid eight of them out on the stainless steel counter to cool and was turned away, rolling more dough. They won't miss just one, right? Ben could duck down, creep up while the cook was turned, nab one, and scoot. I quietly backtracked, ran into Ben and Tim, who'd followed me, and shared my discovery and my idea.

"Ben, if they catch you, they'll just scold you, because you're underage. But if Tim or I get caught, they could charge us," I said, without thinking how cowardly, not to mention stupid, I was being. Tim agreed. After Ben's cool response to his detention in Jasper, we were both figuring this wouldn't bother him at all.

His eyes said he was worried, but his lips said, "Sure. I can do it. I'll meet you back on deck afterward."

So much for a plan. As Tim and I backed off to hide in the hallway, Ben crept forward while crouching to the point where he was under the lined-up pies. It was then that I saw what I hadn't before, and I froze in panic. Just above Ben was an angled mirror, with another in front of the cook. Even with his back turned, he could see Ben, but as of yet, Ben didn't know it.

Just as I opened my mouth to speak, Ben popped up, snatched the pie, and scurried out in front of me. The cook was right on Ben's tail, shouting in alarm and racing after him up the staircase and around corners. Tim and I sped after them. I hoped Ben would lay the pie down and keep going, but the cook was closing fast and there wasn't time. When we caught up with them, the cook held Ben by his sleeve with one hand, held the pie in the other, and, red-faced, was yelling, "Just what do you think you're doing, stealing my pies, you thief!"

Tim and I approached to provide support, and a uniformed mate appeared, drawn by the commotion of the chase and the shouting cook. When the cook wound down, the mate, having taken it all in, turned to Ben, asked him his name, and then turned to Tim and me for the same.

"You three may leave now," he said. "We'll be talking to you later." Then he said to the cook, "These boys will be addressed later. But for now, let's get the kitchen back in order."

And with that, he led the cook off. The three of us glumly retreated to our upper deck campsite, mumbling worries about the consequences yet to be faced. They knew who we were, had our names. And we weren't going anywhere. As we steamed south through Stephens Passage, the walls of immense trees on either side we'd been passing for the last ten hours scented our disturbed dreams.

Chapter 24

The MV Wickersham steamed through the night, and in the morning we arrived in Petersburg, somewhat hung over and nervously wondering when the ship's authorities would approach us. We were 200 miles from Haines, about halfway through our sea voyage. We'd be heading into the Wrangell Narrows next, and the ship would be docked for three hours in Petersburg while the tide rose. Because the tides average over 11 feet between high and low, this wait for high tide was necessary to make navigation possible. The gangway was put out to permit passengers to go ashore, and while Tim slept, Ben and I headed for town with a backpack of breakfast ingredients.

Walking along the waterfront, the dominant commercial activity here was obvious. Petersburg, with a population just over 2,000, had four canneries and the fleet of seiners to supply them. The boats were all of a uniform length of about 60 feet and were tied up by the dozens in slips and along the docksides, which twisted with the shoreline. These canneries process over 100 million pounds of fish and shellfish annually, making it the fifteenth most productive port by volume in the U.S. For a short time during a peak period of the commercial fishing industry, Petersburg was rumored to have the highest per–capita income for a working town in the U.S. A bronze statue of a fisherman,

Peter Buschmann, the Norwegian immigrant who founded the town, stood in a small town square. The Norwegian flag flew from a lamppost and postcards nicknamed the town "Little Norway."

Ben and I found a bench in the sun, but out of the way, and lit our gas stove, whipped up a bowl of pancake batter, and started devouring pancakes soaked in syrup.

"What do you think they'll do to us?" Ben asked. It was out of the blue, but it was also near the surface.

"I don't know, Ben. They could have thrown us off the ship, but I'm glad they haven't. I'm surprised the captain or some other authority hasn't approached us. Maybe they'd rather not have to deal with us and are thinking that by having us wait for the other shoe to drop, we'll mind our behavior. Or it's also possible that they've got their hands full with something more important, like running this ship and, aside from keeping an eye on us, don't have further plans."

Ben replied, "I kind of think that if they were going to punish us in some way, they would have done it by now. There are over a thousand other people on board, and some of them might cause more trouble than we have. Whatever it is, I'm glad we haven't been visited yet. I'm nervous just thinking about it."

Ben and I were both thinking, and hoping, the same thing—by keeping a low profile, we could stay in the background and maybe, just maybe, the whole thing would fade away.

"Anyway, these pancakes are the best breakfast I've had for a while. I've had enough oatmeal for a lifetime," Ben added.

I raised my plastic cup of instant coffee, he raised his, and we toasted.

"Here's to a great breakfast," I said. And we both smiled.

Back on board, we found Tim on the forward deck, where he was just finishing a bowl of oatmeal he'd made with hot tap water from the cafeteria. No authorities had visited him while we were ashore. Ben and I looked at each other and raised our eyebrows in hope.

The ship's horn blasted and crewmembers hauled hawsers as the giant props churned froth, pulling the hull from the dock. Within minutes, we entered the Wrangell Narrows, one of the most challenging navigational gauntlets for ferry captains on the Inside Passage. About 20 miles long and averaging about a half mile wide, the Narrows channel squeezes to 300 feet at its narrowest point. The MV Wickersham was 363 feet long and about 80 feet wide. Red buoys on one side and green on the other mark the channel. Ferries travel even in the fog, and every few years a ferry runs aground or hits something. Additionally, the Narrows are only 19 feet deep at low tide at the most shallow point. Our ferry drew 15 feet of water. Now I understood the importance of our three-hour layover in Petersburg.

A crewman arrived on the front deck and took his position in the bow as a lookout. He unlocked and lifted the steel lid of a shallow box located next to a large bell. We learned later that if we were in danger of hitting anything, he would have pressed the emergency anchor switch in the box and rung the bell. At this point, it occurred to me why the captain might have had more on his mind than three young men who stole a pie from the kitchen, and I felt pretty small. There were several small boats in our path, and when one of them got too close, our pilot blasted the horn but didn't change speed or course.

As we sailed south through the Narrows, the shorelines

closed in and, very quickly, there was a lot less room for boats, ships, and creatures to share. The air was crowded with eagles and ospreys and, looking down into the water, we saw why. Schools of huge salmon were at or near the surface, forced there by the whales, visible just beneath them. The humpbacks, about eight of them, swam in the same direction as the salmon, headed north, perhaps as part of their annual 16,000-mile migration. They didn't seem to be in any hurry, nor were they the least bit flustered by the salmon careening all around them.

The whales seemed to be checking with one another, moving as needed to maintain their position. The school of salmon would fracture, sliding to either side of a whale, and their exposure excited the eagles and ospreys. For a brief moment, the water itself became the whales and the salmon, and the air became the eagles and the ospreys, a mass of dynamic life in front of us. Then they were gone, the water suddenly lifeless.

"I think I was just granted super powers for a moment," I said, incredulously. "I saw another world. An incredibly beautiful one."

"That was the most amazing display of marine life I've ever seen," Ben said. "It seemed as though the whales knew exactly what they were doing and were watching out for the salmon, too."

"I felt like I was just another traveler on their highway," I said.

"Which, I guess, we all are," Tim replied. "They've been here a lot longer than we have."

Wrangell took shape in the distance, and we felt the ship slow. Passengers moved toward the gangway. Tim said, "I need to stretch my legs, so I'm going ashore to look around. I'll take a pb and j sandwich with me and some Tang."

"Watch the time, eh?" I said. "There's been no announcement about how long we'll be here, and it may only be long enough to unload and load vehicles and passengers."

"I'll be back in time, don't worry," Tim said, heading for the gangway. Ben held up a pair of crossed fingers and we smiled at each other. Watching Tim cross the dock, I caught sight of the town flag. Above the town seal was the town's name and beneath it the motto read, "Gateway to the Stikine," referring to the river, and the wilderness named after it, which empties into the bay opposite Wrangell Island.

Chapter 25

The Tlingit people, the natives here, have inhabited this island, and all of southeast Alaska, for 10,000 years. According to clan tradition, Tlinglit people migrated down the Stikine River during a time when the river still flowed underneath glaciers. The Tlingit, along with Haida and Tsimshian natives, number over 10,000 of the Tongass's 70,000 people.

The Tlingit developed a complex and elaborate social and economic system focused on the cycles of fish and wildlife resources. The Tongass provides the basis for their cultural values, which are grounded in a spiritual relationship to their environment, including all the living beings of the land, sea, and universe. Anthropologists state that these native communities of southeast Alaska were the most sophisticated, completely subsistence cultures to inhabit the earth.

Their traditional value of "Haa Aani" (our land) expresses the core of their relationship with the land, in both reverence and use. They believe that the land and all living creatures on the earth and in the sea have spirits.

The Tlingit are divided into two major groups, the Eagles and the Ravens, which are then divided into clans, with each clan split into houses. Clan membership and names create bonds with their ancestors, who held the same names, and with future generations, who will also carry these names. This system assures each Tlingit immortality, through those who will carry their names. All members of a clan are taken as being related, even without a biological relationship. They see themselves not just as individuals but also as members of different social units through which they act collectively.

When the Tlingit use any natural resource, they must give thanks to the spirits and describe how the spirits will strengthen their physical and cultural survival. They are obligated to share their bounty with their clan members and with their elders. Children are taught early on about the cultural value of sharing, and they are required to share their first fish or other resources they have caught or gathered with their relatives.

Tlingit territory is potlatch country. People gain status by how much they give away at great feasts. In their language, there is no word for starvation. The Tlingit saying "When the tide is out, our table is set" refers to the bountiful provisions the natural world gives them. Dungeness and king crab, mollusks and shellfish, salmon and halibut abound in their homeland. The Tlingit show their gratitude in their consideration of other creatures as powerful clans with languages, customs, and thoughts of their own. This sense of kinship is easier to understand when you realize the Tlingit are surrounded by record densities of bears, orcas, humpback whales, and Dall's porpoises, all creatures with large brains and cooperative feeding strategies. The fauna in this group also includes wolf packs, beaver colonies, ravens, sea lions, and otters.

Tlingit art evolved from their clan-oriented culture. The images they carve and inscribe identify their individual clans, their houses, and their families. They abstract these designs from the world around them and the animals they encounter in their everyday lives. Their art is totally integrated with their daily existence and decorates their clothing, weapons, boats, and architecture. In the past, they built large, wooden, tribal houses, which could shelter up to 100 tribal members. They also built 60-foot seaworthy canoes, in which they traveled the coast from Prince William Sound to the northern coast of Oregon, about 1,400 miles, trading for goods.

In 1971, with the Alaska Native Claims Settlement Act, Congress recognized natives' aboriginal title to the remaining land in southeast Alaska but actually conveyed title to only a portion of it. Native leaders wanted full ownership of their lands and pursued the settlement with their corporation, Sealaska. They rejected the reservation system, under which the federal government holds lands in trust for other tribes.

Village and urban corporations, which each received 23,000 acres, were established for 13 communities in Southeast Alaska. But Congress did not award land to the natives in five native communities—Haines, Tenakee, Wrangell, Petersburg, and Ketchikan. Even though natives had lived in this area for 10,000 years, they were denied land awards because nonnatives were now the majority of the populations in those communities. Native residents there, over 40 years later, are still seeking their land entitlements in Congress.

Despite four decades of frustration, the Tlingit have kept their vision of what matters.

Chapter 26

After relaxing on board, Ben and I scanned the shore while passengers returned, some with bags of souvenirs. When the bulk of them had boarded and there was still no sign of Tim, Ben and I exchanged nervous looks.

"Hope he shows up soon," Ben said. "There's no way they're going to hold the ship for him."

"I don't suppose it would do any good to ask them to do so, but it might be worth a try," I replied. Just then two crewmembers arrived to pull up the gangway, pausing, as if waiting for a signal to proceed. I walked over to one of them and said, "We've got a brother who went ashore but hasn't returned yet. How long will it be before you cast off?" I asked.

"Just a few minutes. We're waiting for the bell, which is our signal," he replied.

"Is there any way we could request to wait a bit? I'm sure he'll be right along," I said.

"I have to act on the bell. You can try to talk to the captain, but he's expected to keep the ship on schedule."

The way he said it, the situation didn't sound promising, and given our tenuous stance with the pie theft neither Ben nor I wanted to explain how, once again, we were causing problems. The bell rang and the crewmembers began to bring in the gangway.

And then, walking casually into sight, came Tim. We immediately started yelling and waving and two things happened: the crewmembers extended the gangplank and Tim broke into a run. He bound up the gangplank and hit the deck gasping.

"Glad you could make it," Ben said.

"I got sidetracked by the cool stuff in town," Time replied, still panting.

"When you catch your breath, we'd like to hear about it," Ben said.

I approached the crewmember I'd spoken to, who was finishing pulling the gangway in and said, "Thanks for your help. We appreciate it."

"No problem. Glad he arrived," he said.

"We are too," I replied.

I turned to join my brothers and Ben said, "How's about we make some lunch? I'm hungry."

"Me too," Tim said.

"A peanut butter and jelly sounds great," I added. "Let's go." And we headed to the deck area where we'd left our pack, made sandwiches, and soaked up the early afternoon sun.

As the afternoon passed and evening approached, Tim, Ben, and I prepared the dinner we considered a feast: two cans of Dinty Moore Beef Stew heated over our gas stove, accompanied by Wonder Bread and Tang. For dessert, we drank hot tea, ate Oreos, and smoked our beloved hand-rolled cigarettes. The sun was dropping, but still a way from setting as we docked in Ketchikan about six o'clock. Tim was content to read on board, but Ben and I, tired of ship confinement, decided to poke around town.

At first glance, the waterfront looked shabby, off–kilter, swaybacked and disheveled. Some businesses badly needed a coat of paint. Others were poorly lit or presented window displays that hadn't been changed in years. Shops were cramped in alleyways. Creek Street, right off the main street, took its name from Ketchikan Creek, over which shops hung, cantilevered from both sides, a few leaning seriously toward the water. It was damp everywhere, which, given that the town of 7,000 gets over 150 inches of rain a year, wasn't surprising.

But once we'd been walking for a few minutes, we realized that Ketchikan had a rhythm of its own. The diverse and obviously homegrown businesses served locals and seasonal migrations of loggers, fishermen, hunters, and tourists like us. A chainsaw/small engine repair shop was sandwiched between a coffee shop and a drugstore. Farther down, a small grocery store stood next to a bookstore and a tackle/firearms shop. They all looked well patronized. Farther along, we saw a garage, a bank, and a small music store. Along the waterfront perched a couple of busy marinas. Floatplanes rocked in their slips alongside commercial fishing boats. There were even a few sailboats. The Ketchikan Pulp Company mill, on the north shore of Ward Cove, half a mile from town, was the major employer for the region.

We were 364 miles from Haines.

Chapter 27

We returned to the ferry from our tour of Ketchikan, and I realized I hadn't thought of the pending response to our pie heist. With our last stop, Prince Rupert, coming next, we were fast approaching the end of waiting and a reckoning was at hand.

Shortly after we returned to the ship, two uniformed officers with business on their faces approached the three of us. We glanced at each other nervously, figuring this was our sentencing hearing. The older officer spoke first.

"We need to speak with you three regarding complaints about you from other passengers," he said. He motioned off to the side of the passageway, indicating a need for privacy, and we followed his lead. He was in his early fifties we figured, with a ruddy complexion and gray hair beneath his officer's cap. His mate was younger, in his thirties maybe, shorter and thinner. The older man did not introduce himself or his partner, nor did he ask us our names, but continued.

"I've received a number of complaints from passengers who say they've seen you attempting to enter staterooms that aren't yours." With that he looked coolly at each of us. "These complaints have been made seven times over the last two days. The passengers who reported this behavior all identified you, either individually or together, and pointed you out to my fellow officer here," he said, nodding to the younger man. I listened in disbelief, expecting him to continue by saying, "Furthermore, there is the matter of the pie theft."

To my astonishment, he didn't. I could breathe again. I was composing my sentences in this state of relief and, because of it, felt and sounded, at least to myself, calm and confident in our innocence. It was important to be sincere, open, and helpful. Impressions mattered a lot.

"Officer, I don't know who these passengers have seen, but I can assure you that none of us have been involved in that behavior. With the exception of the four dockings so far in our trip, we've all been together, mostly here on the main deck, either eating, reading, sightseeing, or playing ping-pong. When we first boarded, we explored the ship and looked into a cabin that had an open door, but just out of curiosity. And we haven't been below deck because we've had no need." Then Ben took his turn.

"Honestly, officer, we've only moved from the main deck here, where we keep our stuff, to the front deck for a change of view or to the lounge when it's too cold outside, or to use the bathroom. We do feel a need to move about a bit, to offset sitting so much."

Ben held both officers' attention, as they tried to gauge our truthfulness. The younger man was watching me and Tim.

I felt an air of urgency about this gathering, as if the officers not only wanted to resolve the matter on the spot, but also might also be looking for a way to escape the work of actually having to uphold consequences as a result of a discovery of guilt, a way out while still fulfilling their duties as authorities on the ship. Credible testimony, I hoped, would give them enough to satisfy that need.

Recognizing the need for the officers to hear from all of us, Tim contributed, and began by acknowledging the senior officer's authority.

"Sir, my brothers and I may have offended some passengers by laughing or talking too loud or getting too noisy while making our dinner on deck, but for the life of me I can't think of anything else we could have done that might have upset people. (Not the pie? I thought.) We're glad just not to be sitting in the rain and to have a warm place to read or play ping-pong when it's cold out."

There was a pause; the senior officer looked at his younger mate and then at us and said, "All right. Here's what I need from you. I understand you are to disembark at Prince Rupert. That's in six hours, and we'll be arriving around 3:00 a.m. Between now and then, I need your solemn assurance that you will conduct yourselves in a manner that respects other passengers' privacy. Your deportment will be none other than that of the respectful individuals you have stated yourselves to be. I cannot receive a single more complaint without pursuing legal procedure, which would require a referral to the police in Prince Rupert. Do I make myself clear?"

He'd given both himself and us an out, and I was relieved by this solution, which found middle ground while still saving face on both sides. There was no doubting the sincerity of his intentions, either. In the back of my mind, I was also thankful for whatever luck, providence, or oversight omitted our guilt in the pie robbery. It simply never came up, and that was it.

"Yes, sir," each of us stated, with full measures of gravity.

We knew we were free, but also on an edge. The officer had done his job well.

"Well then," he said. "I'll take you at your word. And now, with our business completed, I'll bid you good day."

"Good day," each of us responded, as the two officers walked off. Then we turned to each other with expressions of total surprise and complete relief. It was time for a dinner to celebrate our freedom. But celebrate quietly.

Chapter 28

The remainder of the evening did pass quietly, and we went to bed early, each of us spreading our sleeping bags over lounge chairs under open skies. But even though we remembered our early departure the following morning, none of us thought to set an alarm, and we overslept.

At 3:00 a.m., Tim woke to an impatient voice paging him on the public address system and stumbled to the vehicle deck, where an irate crewman waited for him to start the car. When the weak snaps from the battery weren't enough to turn over the engine, the crewman called for a tractor. The tractor driver, also seething with the middle-of-the-night call, chained the car's rear bumper to his tractor's bucket and lifted the rear of the car. Backing up with the car swaying beneath the bucket, he unceremoniously yanked the car up the ramp.

"Take it easy, will you!" Tim yelled when the car lurched toward the wall in the narrow ramp. The driver ignored him and dropped the car on the dock, hard, before grinding off. Tim fumed. "What a jerk! Did you see that? We'll be lucky if this car ever starts!"

We were all cold and disoriented, blankly staring into the night, dimly trying to come up with a plan. The few other cars that had also left the ferry had all driven off, and the ship was casting off. We called a garage from the pay phone underneath the single street light in the parking lot. They'd come out, but not until 7:00, four hours off, which we declined. A friendly man driving a Renault offered to help us jump-start our car, but although the engine cranked a few turns, the response quickly got weaker, soon producing only the faintest of clicks. Then a taxi driver offered, with pretty much the same result. The third car, another taxi, was the magic, and Tim gunned the engine. The driver declined our offers of payment, and we thanked him profusely before driving away. Our destination: Prince George, about 450 miles southeast on the Yellowhead Highway, the only road to it.

We drove the rest of the night and through the morning, bypassing the town itself on a cut-off, just before noon. Not seeing Prince George didn't matter. We'd forgotten, but we'd seen it before on our way north, weeks earlier. Glad to be moving again after days of waiting in Haines and being confined to the ferry, we pressed on, due south, toward the state of Washington.

Along the way, we drank so much coffee that we launched into an impromptu skit with three parts, each contributing nonsensical, high-speed gibberish that kept us occupied for hours. We even carried it into convenience stores when we gassed up, where, though toned down considerably, we drew odd looks from customers and clerks. At one store near Quesnel, British Columbia, we bought five loaves of white bread and six pounds of peanut butter for $3.58, which triggered a hyperactive run of ridiculous chatter, in multiple accents, culminating in uncontrollable laughing fits. We'd gone bona fide road crazy. We also happened to be only about 100 miles, as the crow flies, west of Jasper, Alberta, where we had spent time in court for one offense and escaped it for another the same day, just over three weeks ago. The shop lifting and attempted trout heist seemed like years ago.

Six tanks of gas farther south on the Cariboo Highway, late at night, we reconnected with the Trans–Canada Highway, in southern British Columbia, and followed it to Abbottsford, on the U.S. border. At the time, The Trans–Canada was the longest uninterrupted highway in the world, spanning nearly 5,000 miles. We'd driven over three quarters of it.

At customs, the Canadians waved us through with the friendliness of those who don't have to clear your passage into their country. The U.S. officials, having first dispensed with the standard set of questions, then instructed us to pull over and step out of the car. Our appearance, and the state of the vehicle, drew the attention.

We'd just driven over 900 miles straight, and our expressions were plastered with road haze. We hadn't showered or shaved in a couple of weeks, had been wearing the same clothes for at least that time, while sleeping outdoors for over a month. My blue jeans and sweatshirt could stand up on their own and my brothers' would have also. Long, greasy, and uncombed, our hair needed industrial treatment.

The interior of the car was a rabbit warren of belongings. Clothes, lunch supplies, water bottles, cigarette rolling materials, three loose sleeping bags, flashlights, several maps, and stray camping utensils of all sorts littered the inside. Coffee cups, thermoses, wrappers, corn nut and bacon rind bags, and paper bags of various sizes covered the floor. The ashtray was overflowing. The dashboard was stacked with brochures, the atlas, the journal, paperbacks, and cigarette papers and tobacco. The rear window deck held wool caps, mittens, and an extra sweater. Noticeably absent were any sunglasses, shorts, or bathing suits.

The customs officers rooted in this disorder while we stood on the sidewalk, in the middle of the night, tired, but confident. The last of the weed had been inhaled weeks ago; there wasn't even any beer in the car. The agents shared their checklist, once in a while shot us a suspicious scowl, and then gutted the trunk. Fortunately, it hadn't been disturbed much in the last week, but the two of them took every tackle box apart, unfolded every tin foil package of hooks, and even inspected any dry foodstuffs, like spaghetti and flour. After about 15 minutes, they told us we could go.

Crossing the line into the States, even in the dark, I had a strong sense of returning home. Although we still had thousands of miles yet to travel, we were back in familiar territory. I'd even been in Washington just three years before, visiting a friend near Olympic National Park, where we were headed now.

I was driving when we reached Seattle, about three a.m. After swirling around on the city's cement ribbons, searching for the ferry terminal, we finally found it and caught the next ferry across Puget Sound to the Olympic peninsula. The ferry dropped us at Winslow as the sun was rising, and I kept driving. Four hours west, we arrived in Port Angeles, where friends of mine lived. I drove up the park road to Hurricane Ridge, a landmark from my previous trip to see them, and we walked from the trailhead out along the ridge.

After days of being cooped up waiting for the ferry and then more days confined to the ship, and then driving over 1,000 miles, the open expanse of the distant view was liberating. Alpine meadows, strewn with blooming wildflowers under full sun, sloped off in all directions. Hiking got our blood pumping again and stretched our long-cramped legs. We had landed at a place to explore and to discover, with room to enjoy.

Small groups of deer grazed nearby. When we approached slowly, they only moved off when we got within touching distance. A marmot patrolled his den opening, also comfortable with our proximity. He watched us with curiosity for a while and when convinced we were benign, went about his business. It was the blue grouse, though, that drew our attention with their naiveté. Tim calmly approached one that was feeding nearby in the meadow, and when it didn't move off, he carefully closed the distance, curious about just how close he could get. The grouse stood still and Tim got within a step of it, crouched, and picked it up. Ben and I joined him, murmured to the bird, and quietly enjoyed a rare moment of complete trust with a wild creature.

It reminded me of an afternoon in the spring, perhaps ten years earlier, when I was walking home from the bus stop after school. A covey of chickadees had been leap-frogging me along the road as I walked. As an experiment, I halted and extended my hand to them. When the bird lit on my outstretched fingers, I felt tiny pencil points of grasping claws and the faint brush of feather to skin. I also felt anointed, the St. Francis of Goodhill Road, and floated the remainder of my walk home in complete serenity.

Tim gently returned the blue grouse to its spot on the ground and we tiptoed away, quietly reflective after our surge up the trail.

Returning to town, we stopped at a campground and took

showers. It took me three rinses and a handful of quarters to wash my hair. For the first time in weeks, we were squeaky clean. Back in town, I found a quiet place to park and sleep while Tim and Ben looked around Port Angeles. After their tour, we found a laundromat. Clean clothes felt pounds lighter. For dinner, we met up with my friend, Bill Grubb, and his wife, Terry, at their house. Being in a home after so long was a rapid shift of re-immersion into the everyday world.

The radio alone brought a sudden return to the world of airwaves: pop music, commercials, news, and incessant chatter. David Bowie urged us to turn and face the change, the Eagles advised us not to let the sound of our own wheels drive us crazy, and Paul Simon comforted us with the news that the mother-child reunion was only a motion away. David's directive echoed the rum-runner's, although the courage to face the change was daunting. Glen Frey's advice spoke to exactly what I seemed to be doing—driving myself crazy. And a reunion with my mother would be a life-changing breakthrough, not just for myself, but also for Tim, Ben, and our sister, Tamsen, as well.

Tim and I had run from her drinking and the life it created at home, first to the local rivers, which became our refuge. By middle school, we'd run from home and stayed away, spending nights in the woods. The Child Welfare Department intervened and placed us in a Jesuit school for boys in Albany. Most of the students had been abandoned by their parents. After three months, we were released to a couple back in our hometown, who became our foster parents. Although I'd visited my mom over the years, I hadn't spent a night back at home since.

Ben, too young to run with us, had stayed and experienced his own exile, in Bev's continued drinking and her resultant neglect. Tamsen had found that boyfriends were a way out of the house and spent more time with them as she got older. She resented Tim and me for having left home. I'd seen her only rarely over our high school and college years, and even then, distractedly. The distances between her and both of us were lonely spaces, fraught with distrust and self–preservation.

Within two years of our placement in the foster home, Tim's friction with our foster father, over Tim's minor delinquencies, exploded in several, violent, fits–of–rage beatings, and Tim returned to live with Mom. I'd been away from all three of my siblings through high school and college.

I was beginning to realize that this trip fishing together, though helpful, wasn't going to be enough to span the gap of those formative years. To expect that to happen with one trip together, no matter how grand, was unrealistic.

This realization landed hard, but with the comfort that hard truth brings. Suddenly, you're released from the dream of hoping or wishing for something you want. You know that all the striving isn't going to bring you any closer to your hope, and all the heartache of that desire falls away. It was a gift of the journey.

I'd been looking for another truth, a shiny, more optimistic one that allowed me to believe we would all recover those lost years apart and simply renew the bonds of our childhood before the family had fallen apart. But we'd shared too many dark times back then and hadn't built a stock of common experiences since. We'd have to build that over our adult years, if we could. At least, I thought, our trip might be a start toward that reunion.

Chapter 29

After a terrific dinner with my friends Bill and Terry, we drove back into Olympic Park, where a friendly ranger escorted us to a free campsite on the Elwha River. In the morning, Bill and Terry picked us up for a hike to some trout fishing on a more remote section of the river. We followed the river upstream for about four miles, nearly to the Lower Elwha Dam. We walked through the towering temperate rain forest, giant old-growth spruce and hemlock soaring skyward, saved from logging by the creation of Olympic Forest Preserve in 1897, which became a national park in 1938. It was the Tongass before the clear-cutting began, undisturbed forest with a canopy 200 feet up, filtering sunlight, a green, open forest floor smothered in moss and cathedral silence.

Although the forest had been preserved, the river had been sacrificed to hydro-electric generation when two dams, the Lower Elwha and the Glines, eight miles above it, were built in 1913 and 1924. The electricity powered the pulp mill in Port Angeles. The dams were built without fish ladders, and salmon and steelhead were blocked for 70 miles of river and tributaries, 90 percent of their habitat. Ten different runs of the five species of salmon returned each year before the dams, as well as cutthroat trout, native char, and steelhead. The Chinook run alone totaled around 400,000 annually, with many fish over 100 pounds. They were some of the richest salmon runs outside Alaska.

After the dams were built, the run fell to 3,000 fish or fewer. The entire ecosystem collapsed. The Hallam tribe, which had lived on the river for thousands of years, lost the major source of their sustenance, and their culture withered. This tragic story was repeated with scores of rivers in Washington, Oregon, and California. But with the decline of the pulp industry, the need for electricity fell. The Elwha turbines, functioning at a much-reduced level, were deemed unnecessary. In 1992, Congress authorized both dams' removal and restoration of the ecosystem.

After two decades of planning, the largest dam removal in U.S. history began in September of 2011. Elwha Dam was gone six months later, followed by the Glines Canyon Dam in 2014. Within two weeks of the last blast at the Glines Dam, salmon and trout were migrating upstream beyond the former dam site for the first time in 100 years. Although the salmon runs will never recover their full former glory, it's estimated that, within one to five generations, (two to twenty years), a persistent, self-sustaining salmon population will be established.

Active rebuilding of the ecosystem includes bank restoration with tree planting, limiting sediment through revegetation, and careful monitoring of mammal populations, and it will be ongoing in the years ahead. Many stakeholders, including biologists, foresters, the Hallam tribe, the U.S. Fish and Wildlife Service, and environmentalists are scrutinizing the process and the changes. The results of the Elwha River restoration are already providing lessons for restoring fish migrations after dams are removed, and they can be applied to the thousands of now useless dams all over the country still standing that continue to destroy bountiful spawning runs, only because of inertia or lack of funding.

On the Elwha River, the mysteries and meanings in life have returned with the fish.

Chapter 30

While Bill, Tim, and Ben fished, I wandered the old growth forest, marveling at the towering trunks, many over 200 feet tall, 10 feet wide, and thousands of years old. The mats of centuries-old moss and lichen that covered the forest floor were spongy underfoot, busy within their layers with decomposition and soil formation. The decomposers and the elements of climate, both in a huge scale, combine to metabolize organic matter, forming the rich soil that feeds the trees, not only completing the cycle but also making it tangible. This earth was living, dying, and regenerating made manifest, so quietly, yet so powerfully vibrant as to evoke reverence.

I eventually circled my way back to our campsite, where Terry was reading the Bhagavad Gita, the collection of verses from Hindu scripture. Like me, she'd been an English major in college. Also like me, and many of our peers, she'd read many of the authors whose works focused on meaning, direction, and purpose in life. Our common list of writers included Herman Hesse, Alan Watts, Aldous Huxley, Timothy Leary (as Ram Dass), Lao Tzu, Emerson, and Thoreau.

These writers, as philosophers, addressed the questions the burgeoning youth culture of the 1960s and 1970s was asking itself about the search for meaning in life. Specifically, many of us were looking for the way to become ourselves. Beyond earning a living, we strove for satisfaction with who we were. Terry and I shared that search for understanding and awareness. The quest is universal and, at the same time, personal, and I believed that answering it, or the process of trying to, would lead me to the best use of my life. But I wasn't familiar with the Bhagavad Gita and I asked her to explain it to me.

Written in Sanskrit over 2,000 years ago as Hindu scripture, the narrative describes a dialogue between Prince Arjuna and his guide, Lord Krishna. Newly aware that his enemies are his own relatives, beloved friends, and revered teachers, Arjuna is filled with doubt on the battlefield. He turns to his guide and charioteer, God Incarnate Lord Shri Krishna, for advice. Krishna responds to Arjuna's confusion and moral dilemma by explaining to Arjuna his duties as a warrior and a prince. Within this urge for chivalry is a discussion about the ways of attaining self-realization.

Terry then read a quote from the book jacket. "The Bhagavad Gita," she said, quoting Jawaharlal Nehru, "is a call of action to meet the obligations and duties of life, yet keeping in view the spiritual nature and grander purpose of the universe." With regard to the question of whether to engage with the world or renounce it, the Bhagavad Gita values energy, dedication, and selfless service. As an active person, this made much sense to me. What forms my action, dedication, and service would take, however, were still mine to choose. But at least I was beginning to understand that my choices would inform me themselves and provide the best guide to finding my path. The next step was to commit to something.

Tim, Ben, and Bill returned from their outing with a dozen

pan-sized trout. We built a fire and collected green branches, which we wove into grilling cages. The fish cooked quickly and we ate them just as fast on fire-toasted bread, leaving us all still hungry. When Bill suggested that we all head back to their place for steelhead steaks, we jumped at the chance for another home-cooked meal.

We dowsed the fire and hiked out in the twilight, sighting a couple of bears on the mountainside opposite our trail. As we watched, they ambled from one grazing spot to another, much as we were doing, but sustained only by wild provisions. Our attempts to do the same kept us connected to the wilderness, and to them. Those choices continued as Terry and Bill prepared the steelhead steaks from fish Bill had caught, as well as salad greens and potatoes they had grown in the yard near their trailer. For them, this dining was the norm, not the exception, with the nearby ocean providing Dungeness crab and clams as well. After midnight, and now fully stuffed, we said goodnight.

In the morning, we returned to Bill and Terry's for our final thanks and goodbyes and headed for La Push, on the coast. Bill and Terry had told us of the old-growth rain forest there, which ran right to pristine beaches. A 60-mile length of the coast, only a few miles wide, which is part of, though not connected to, Olympic National Park, has beaches with unbroken stretches of wilderness ranging from 10 to 20 miles long. There are so many beaches that few have names, just numbers. Coming from heavily developed East coast beaches, where it was difficult to get shore access without a hefty day-use fee, we longed for surf undeveloped and open to all.

We arrived at Third Beach trailhead in the late afternoon, stuffed our packs with all we could carry for a comfortable overnight, and hiked toward the shore. Lurching under our loads, we were grateful for the springy rain forest floor and the shade provided by the immense Sitka spruce, Coast Douglas fir, hemlock, and cedar, much as in the Tongass. Mosses coated their bark and dangled from their branches in green tendrils.

The groves of giant trees grew right to the sand, resulting in large chunks of timber from fallen trees on the beach. Massive trunks, some 10 feet in diameter, lay stacked or strewn about, some high and dry, others still partially afloat. These fallen beach trees were joined by logs, tops, root wads, and sunken or partially submerged logs called deadheads, discharged from the peninsula's western rivers and then moved north with current up the coast. The combination of naturally eroded timber and other drift enriches the water with tremendous amounts of organic matter, much as they do in rivers.

The commanding presence of these driftwood deposits showed us plainly what beaches looked like before colonization. The removal of this driftwood from streams and beaches was a major domestication measure across North America, and the construction of thousands of dams prevented much of any further driftwood from reaching the ocean. In our effort to clean up beaches and control rivers, we have impoverished both and ourselves as well. Standing on Third Beach we could, for the first time, feel the border where the Pacific meets North America as the sacred wilderness it once was.

We clambered all over this wonderful tangle of beached forests, climbed a cliff, and walked the sand until tired. Beside the trunk of a fallen giant, we built a fire, cooked dinner, and fell asleep to the crashing, pounding rhythm of the surf. We never saw another soul.

Chapter 31

That solitude was the prime ingredient in my early days of fishing. My most prized possession was my fishing rod. It was a gift I gave myself and was a survival tool, a device for self-expression and a key to the peaceful world I needed.

There were three parts: the rod, the reel, and the line. The rod couldn't be too long and needed to be balanced and to have an even flex throughout its arc, without any flat sections. I preferred a cork handle with sliding double rings. That way you could move the reel up or down the handle to suit your own sense of balance.

The reel had to be an open-faced spinning reel; closed-face reels were constrictive and prevented full expression of your casting precision. An adjustable drag was important also, to help you slow the large fish down.

The line had to be between 4 and 6-pound test. Heavier and it restricted your casting, lighter and it snarled easily, nor would it allow for real hefty tugging when you got snagged.

The whole setup, known as "my rod," took a pounding on my handlebars as I biked to and from my spots on the river. My rod was something that gave me adventure, led me to other worlds, and let me forget our family life. I took care of it.

You got a new one only when the old one was broken

beyond repair and you had saved enough from paper routes and raking leaves. A break usually, and all too frequently, occurred in the jaws of a waiting door, in a house or sometimes in a car, or could even occur during the course of cross–country biking escapades by getting into just the wrong spot.

If it broke at the tip, the best repair was to remove the tiptop, the line guide at the top, and try to fit it onto the broken rod, discarding the broken piece of rod. If the rod shaft was too wide to fit the old tiptop onto it, you had to get a larger diameter tiptop and glue it onto the rod, making sure to line it up properly with the other guides. Special glue for this, guide cement, came as a candle. You heated it with a match and then smeared it onto the broken rod tip. The resulting rod was functional, but without the missing section it was shorter and stiffer. Feeling the action at the other end of the line was a bit trickier then. But it sufficed until the day when I'd saved enough and was able to buy a new rod.

When we fished posted property, the most troublesome worry was: What if I get caught and they take my rod away, a fate Tim suffered more than once. That thought was powerful enough to ensure us using the utmost stealth, usually slipping into the forbidden water during the predawn hours. This meant that we had to leave home early enough and either ride bikes or walk. Early enough was usually between three and four in the morning. An hour's travel would bring us to streamside in time to sneak in under the cover of darkness and be casting to waiting monsters as the sun was rising. Darkness was a cover for admission, but it brought its own problems.

First of these were dogs. Neighborhood dogs that wouldn't look twice at you riding by in the light of day would go berserk if they sensed your presence during the night. The ensuing racket always brought the threat of discovery. Then you'd either have to run (or ride) for it, or answer to an angry adult. We did everything in our power, including riding well out of our way, to avoid houses where we knew alarm dogs lived. No talking when passing these houses. Stay low. Avoid any noise at all costs. Coast as much as you could.

We could never tell for sure where these dogs might be, as the cast of characters changed frequently. Consequently, we traveled the whole distance as quietly as our skills allowed, in perpetual vigilance against detection.

Having to be so ever mindful of our noise level taught us what was possible and showed us the benefits of vigilance. Because there was no talking between us, we each had to travel as if solo, using only visual cues or hand gestures to communicate. You had to watch each other for signals and observe closely, all senses alert, scanning for potential trouble around each curve.

We were also blessed with the sights of the hour: the nighttime sky ablaze with stars and, later, the day creeping in as dawn's eye opened. Often we'd catch nocturnal animals on the move: skunks, opossums, deer, or raccoons surprised by our sudden, silent appearance. These sights were part of the reward. You knew you were seeing things that others, asleep, wouldn't.

To avoid the paved roads as much as possible, we'd take shortcuts through the fields, over stone walls, hefting our bikes and rods like voyageurs making a portage. We came to know the topography of our town well and developed a dependable sense of direction. In our efforts to forge new routes, we didn't always know exactly where we'd come out. But we had a rough idea and were willing to give new directions a try, ready for what the land had to teach us, about the lay of the earth and the contours of our character. I was proud knowing I could set out and return safely, usually with fish, without asking for an adult's help, which was out of the question. This was not just our adventure. It was our declaration of independence.

But it was precisely because we had to do it all ourselves that we developed self-reliance and problem-solving skills. If your bike broke down in the middle hours of the night or you gashed your shin on a rock in a stone wall, you were left to yourself to cope. These were our self-administered tests of survival, our invented rites of passage.

We didn't always fish on posted property, but even to fish legal water you needed to arrive early if you expected to succeed. Early morning fishing simply worked best. Once the sun rose to steeper angles, the fishing fell off and it was time to head home.

By then, the tension of the night ride had evaporated with the morning mist. We were dealing with an awakened world and were just boys on their bikes with their fishing rods. We'd arrive home before noon, tired but fulfilled, brimming with discoveries, banking new memories. It always seemed like we'd already lived the day, which we had.

Someone would ask, "How was the fishing?" And whether we'd caught anything or not, we'd always say, "Great."

Chapter 32

In the morning, we said goodbye to the Pacific Ocean, knowing we'd be headed eastward from now on. We were anxious to fish Yellowstone, the Tetons, and Rocky Mountain National Park, and this was our launching point for those hallowed waters.

Yet we were also aware that we were running out of money, that Ben's return to school was approaching, and that our trip home would entail days of driving. With this urgency looming, we'd have to cover ground and cut expenses to essentials only. What we'd see until the parks we'd see from the car. This was settled without much dialogue. After we visited the parks, we knew we'd be heading directly home. They were our last have–to–see places.

Tim drove the six hours from La Push to The Dalles, Oregon, following the Columbia River for over 140 miles. At our gas stop in The Dalles, Oregon, I took over the driving. Having Ben take a turn at the wheel on these crowded U.S. highways wasn't wise. Tim crawled into the hovel in the back seat for a nap, and Ben and I watched the afternoon sun shimmer on the flat water of the Columbia as we said goodbye to The Dalles. For 90 miles, the Columbia's slack water, behind the dams, kept us company heading east. Over 200 of the dams in the river basin are 100 feet or higher, with many more of all sizes in the entire watershed. With the dams, the river had become a dead zone, without movement or migration, unable to fulfill its sacred purpose.

The road left the Columbia at Boardman, Oregon, and turned south, rising through the Blue Mountains to La Grande and then dropping into Baker City, where it crosses the Oregon Trail. Tim woke and fixed us peanut butter sandwiches for dinner, with Tang as a chaser. We gassed up, stretched our legs, and I got back in the driver's seat.

We chatted for a while about the iconic fishing destinations filling our fantasy agenda: the Madison, the Fire Hole, the Gallatin, the Gibbon, and the Snake, which has its headwaters just inside Yellowstone Park on the Two Ocean Divide, at a point on the Continental Divide. These were the streams we'd read about for years in the angling magazines and books, and we savored the idyll we held of their beauty and their trout. These, our final fishing memories of this odyssey, would send us homeward and perhaps even toward an adult life as friends and companions.

By 7:30 p.m., we'd crossed into Idaho, the Plymouth rolling east into the oncoming evening. Except for our night at La Push, it had been running pretty much nonstop since Prince Rupert, nearly 2,000 miles back. The tire repaired with a rubber plug in Val d'Or, Quebec, 9,000 miles ago, still held. We'd somehow partially repaired the window. It still wouldn't close all the way, but its two-inch opening was bearable. The radio, having delivered one verse of Led Zeppelin as we entered Alaska, was still silent. We'd removed the windscreen while waiting for the ferry in Haines, and noted the cracks and chips in the windshield and dings in the hood.

Most important, we managed to splint the exhaust pipe to the muffler with a jury-rigged assembly of hose clamps and an empty bean can. Two spools of wire reinforced the repair and served as exhaust hangers, replacing the ones that had fallen to the battering of the AlCan. The exhaust still wasn't silent, or even quiet. To hear or be heard, the rear passenger had to lean over the front seat and the two front passengers had to speak up. But our ship was still afloat, and the engine ran smoothly as we sailed into the night.

When we rolled through Boise, the country opened into the long-distance views of undulating potato farms, visible now in the fading light. Traffic thinned following the rush hour, and the highway drew an arrow-straight vector toward Twin Falls, near the bottom of our pendulum-swing across the state. Our conversation was intermittent now, with long silences between comments. Each of us, wrapped in our own musings, stared out our windows. Isolated comments were acknowledged with single-syllable mumbles, and the flicker of conversation would fade. As the night deepened, not everyone would respond, as the long, hot day in the car, the monotony of the highway, and the droning of the engine slowly brought drowsiness.

When I pulled in for gas at Twin Falls around midnight, Tim and Ben roused themselves to help out, rolling cigarettes under the station's lights and washing the bug-splattered windshield. I got a cup of coffee inside when I paid for the gas and then we were all back in the car in the same seats. Within a few minutes, I could hear Ben crawl into a sleeping bag in the back seat, saying as he did so, "Just going to catch a few zees, Buck. Let me know if you need more ciggys."

"Will do, Ben. Sweet dreams."

Shortly thereafter, Tim leaned into a pillow against the window and stretched out as much as he could. "I'll be right here, Buck. Just give me a shout if you need me to spell you at the wheel."

"No problem. I got a large coffee. I'll be fine."

The Snake River Plains, an ocean of featureless expanse, stretched without end in all directions into the night, minus even the rolling swales we'd come through. Between the flat land, the black night, the forever-straight dividing line, the monotone engine, the relentless aqua green light of the instrument panel, and the white noise of road wind through the window crack, within minutes, I fell into a world of sensory deprivation. Unmoored, my mind started to drift, at first retrieving memories that would provide needed stimulation, then later creating them.

In pondering my connection with my brothers, the most important ritual we shared and the one at the root of this trip was opening day of trout season. By itself, it encompassed all we had encountered and enjoyed, explored, and discovered together. Its anticipation alone drove us to common plotting, planning, scheming, and organizing far beyond that which we individually employed.

We started with two known facts: Opening Day was always on the third Saturday in April, and we were going to the river to fish. Past that lay every possible outcome, all of which we either attempted to achieve or strove to avoid.

In the beginning, we were all worm fishers, and ensuring a full supply of garden hackles was the first order of business. We'd scour our neighborhood days beforehand, collecting the best specimens we could uncover. We shunned night crawlers for their lack of squirm and because they had filled the discarded styrofoam containers that often littered the riverbanks, and with which we did not want to be associated. Instead, we sought garden worms, shorter and thinner, with superior writhing life underwater. On a size 10 hook, we'd skewer two or three, although more wasn't always better.

Productive worm-gathering sites sometimes held over from year to year, but we couldn't count on them and were constantly searching for new sources. The dependable ones included the spaded earth under the apple tree beside the garage, a collection of small boulders we could turn over, and leaf beds, especially those under eaves without gutters or within the clustered stems of the forsythia. A small coffee can was the largest container we could carry on our bikes, and when the worms ran out on the river we'd search the ground nearby for recruits. But worms were much harder to find along the river, and leaving your casting spot cost you fishing time and, worse, usually your spot itself.

Tramping the woods and fields in our quest enveloped us in the smells of dew-soaked spring mornings: moist, newly heaved earth, moss, and life sprouting. Pungent skunk cabbage reeked in the wetlands and mingled with the verdant aroma of ferns and barberry at the forest's edge, dripping limbs and branches, and the dank scent of wet sneakers. Every spade-struck root, sprout, rotting leaf, particle of sand, and smidgeon of soil released its olfactory load, the bold organicity of vernal urgency.

On opening day, where you were standing was important. Because the stocking trucks had so much river to plant with trout, their crews stopped at bridges and other places where the road was close to the water. Later in the season you'd find fish out of sight of the road, when the stocking crews had time to lug their buckets further. On opening day, though, the pools near the asphalt were the target zones, and they were always crowded.

To claim a prime spot, we had to arrive before the mob, which meant rising by 3:00 a.m., slurping our cereal and banana, and slipping out the door to our bikes. Leaving by 4:00 a.m., we could arrive at a few different places within an hour's ride (the choice of which we had debated the night before) and have our pick of casting spots. Without waders we were at a distinct disadvantage, able to cover only the water we could reach from the riverbank. Staking the best perch on land was therefore critical and also the prime motivator for rising early. Success came mostly in low-light conditions, and you had to be well situated before the sun was on the water.

Approaching on our bikes, we could always hear the river before we saw it. We strained in anticipation of the wonderful racket. The rolling turbulence of the main current stood out, followed by the more muted sections: the purling in the eddies, the surge of slapping at the bank, the bursting spray of the small plunge pools, the local roar of the riffles, the sweeping rush at the bends. The redwing black birds scolded from tree limbs, joined by the swooping ratchet of kingfishers.

Vehicles lined the road, sometimes on both sides near these spots, well before the official start at 6:00 a.m. Almost always American made, they typically included a majority of pickups, some with tradesmen's logos and often rusting, plus a smattering of small sedans, vans, and station wagons. Absent were the British, German, or Swedish badges; drivers here weren't members of the country club. They were all men, from younger, hip boot and camo-clad fellows to middle-aged, cigar-smoking guys in chest waders and knee boots, to the old codgers, the wizened gray-hairs in waders and vests, with wading staffs and landing nets hanging down their backs. Sometimes they were even smoking pipes.

They had come from fisherman's breakfasts, hosted at the local fire department and usually staffed by Boy Scouts, or had driven long distances in darkness to arrive in time to claim a choice spot.

Their equipment was much like ours: spinning rods, though longer, and capable of smacking the water across the river with large lures or gobs of night crawlers, complete with bobbers and split shot. They were the longbow archers, launching their payloads in cross-river arcs. We were the knights' pages, trying to compete with stealth and guile. They came in clanking, noisy hordes, carpeted the water with their missiles, and slaughtered stringers full of naïve, hatchery-fresh trout. We arrived on foot or bike, cast to single spots, and released most of what we caught. They left styrofoam containers, formerly holding coffee or night crawlers, and birds' nests of tangled monofilament, along with lures, bobbers, and split shot dangling from the riverside branches. We departed with a prized trout or two.

As kids far outnumbered, we had to navigate the territory of adults and their etiquette of fishing space. Some of them would actively repel those they thought were encroaching on what they saw as their water. They'd swing expansive casts beyond the reasonable boundaries of their wedge in preemptive strikes, keeping neighboring anglers at bay. Out of their hearing, we called these men "Bridgeporters," for the nearest polluted, decrepit city we, in our heads, were sure they came from. To their faces, we called them "Mister" or "Sir" and they called us "Son" or "Sonny" and even "Boy." They, for their part, had paid the taxes that financed the hatcheries that raised the trout that we both coveted. They had also bought fishing licenses, while we underagers escaped the state's fee. Most wanted only what they felt they were entitled to and were determined to bring it home. I couldn't hold that against them.

Even though we all arrived early, the official start time was 6:00 a.m. and everybody honored that. We'd wait, watching the men arrive and take their positions.

And we'd scan the river for signs of promise: the swing-back swirl of a sharp eddy, spinning foam, insects, hemlock needles and shards of bark, or the isolated and hidden dinner plates of flat water, harboring holding trout. We'd also scout the wide, shallow riffles suddenly emptying into depths, the undercut banks bristling with submerged roots, and the bubbling pockets beneath falls, circulating back onto themselves.

At some point the pool was surrounded by at least a dozen guys, along with latecomers on the fringes upstream or down, all waiting. Someone would mutter something like, "It must be six by now," and the arcs of monofilament would enmesh the river.

Usually Ben or Tim or I would hook up in the first barrage of casting, as did some anglers around us. We all watched one another, keeping tabs and noting where the fish were being caught. You'd hear the splash, find the bent rod, and then, pulling the fish to the net, you'd hear an excited, "Yes, it's a brownie," or a less enthusiastic, "Oh, a brookie."

Brown trout were usually bigger, and it was widely felt that they were wary, wilder, and more difficult to catch; brook trout were considered easy, often smallish, and branded with a reputation closer linked to the hatchery. A brook trout a full foot long was an exception and notable for its size, whereas a brown trout that length was more common, but still notable, not for its size but because it was a brown trout.

The logic wasn't lost on us: brown trout were bigger and therefore older and therefore wiser. The angler who caught one had superior skills. Brook trout, shrimpy and gullible, required less skill or experience and were therefore better suited for children. Fishing was, from this point of view, more about the opportunity to affirm the dominance of the fisher than about the nobility of the quarry or the endeavor to catch them. We knew beforehand the reaction of the adult next to us when we caught a brown and he a brook trout: "Aren't you a *lucky* kid?" Fortunately for us, the trout didn't see it this way and were more egalitarian in their engagement.

We were also wise to the irony of this discrimination, although we had no idea what "irony" was. But we did see flaws in this reasoning, derived from facts we'd learned through our dedication. We knew there were two strains of brown trout, one originating in Scotland, the other in Germany, and both were introduced in North America in the nineteenth century. They grew bigger than brook trout, not because they were more intelligent or wily but because, from their point of origin, they had evolved genes that would let them withstand higher water temperatures than brook trout. This allowed them more opportunities for feeding and growth and, consequently, a longer season for growth and a shorter one for dormancy. In

North America, they were a successful nonnative species, earnestly reared by hatchery men for their boost to "angler hours."

Brook trout were the only native trout, having evolved in eastern North America after the last ice age, 11,000 years ago, and their Latin name indicates that origin. Salvelinus fontinalis, meaning "of the spring, or fountain," is actually a char, along with arctic char, lake trout, and Dolly Varden, the natives of the far north. Brook trout were born in the Laurentian Shield runoff, where short growing seasons and their genetics limited their size at maturity. Their eastern habitat had been degraded to the point where it was necessary to raise them artificially to supplement their wild populations.

Rainbows, which we also caught, were imported from their native streams in the West during the nineteenth century, prized for their leaping and strength. Like brown trout, they adapted, reproduced in their new home, and were also raised in hatcheries.

The mayflies all trout fed on had been hatching for a quarter of a billion years before the dinosaurs browsed in tropical landscapes, long before there were trout. Opening Day was our connection to that great wheel of time, and somehow we knew it.

Tim, Ben, and I all landed our share of these three kindred trout and began to develop an inclusive view. All trout were welcome as the gifts they were. Trout became beings you had to be worthy of catching, and it was through this honoring of our quarry that we knew we could come to know them and ourselves, the world and our place in it. We came to see their beauty and the beauty in the river and all its life forms, especially the water, which supported those life forms and was bigger than all of us. This thought path led us outward, into the world at large, through the doors of wonder.

The opening day goal was for each of us to catch our limit, five trout six inches or longer. My 11-year-old hand span was exactly that, and it determined which trout I could keep. The second digit of my index finger measured one inch, handy for showing just how much past the minimum each trout stretched. On the stream, we'd signal one another across the river, a sly extension of fingers imparting the critical tally.

In the beginning, the score was important. In my single-minded focus, I once caught thirteen trout from the same rock and was repeatedly asked by incredulous anglers around me why I was letting them go. "So I can catch them again when they're bigger" was a reply they couldn't argue with, and it helped to reduce their pestering. But though I liked the idea of releasing a fish to possibly catch it again later when it was bigger, I actually didn't know why I let the trout go, except that it seemed like the right thing to do. Something inside me told me they were too precious, that increasing their number was the goal, not the opposite. As part of the wild, their contact bestowed a vestige of just how bountiful the natural world had once been, before "progress" had begun to dismantle it.

After the first couple of hours, we could feel the collective sigh as the sun rose and the tension along the banks began to loosen up. Anglers began to move, the crowd thinned slightly, and more chatter among the fishermen was audible as they shared plans. We moved also or not, depending on how we'd been doing.

If we did shift our location, it was usually toward the less trampled riverbanks, away from other fishermen. Sometimes we'd move to another favorite spot. Occasionally we'd strike out into never-been-there-before territory, especially when our need to catch trout was less pressing than our need to explore new ground. This was how we discovered fertile spots and also how we'd hone our ability to read water. Catching trout where you knew they'd been stocked was basic. Catching even one trout from water you'd never fished before was a notable achievement, and if you pulled it off, much more rewarding. It also prepared us for the advance of the season, when stocking would fade, eventually to nothing, and landing one trout anywhere became much more challenging in the lower, warmer water of late spring and early summer.

Two rivers, the Saugatuck and the Aspetuck, one with two branches, flowed through our town and in many ways became my parents, guiding me through childhood and adolescence with both their examples and their lessons from the natural world. I looked to them and their trout for inspiration, reward, and the stuff of dreams. From them, I shaped my outlook and myself. My success required work and devotion, sacrifice, and loss. I was a lucky boy. Something connected, between the natural world and myself, and I knew where I belonged, where I truly lived, and it wasn't just in a house.

The rivers bore me outward to the house of the earth, with no roof or floor, no address apart from rivers and mountains or oceans and stars. In my plain thinking as a young boy, I put it this way: the earth is enough, and, embracing it firmly, I'd be okay.

Chapter 33

By now, I was pretty much alone on the highway, with a single car passing in the other direction at long intervals. Sometimes, lost in my thoughts, I'd only become aware that a car had passed when its distant taillights in the rear-view mirror startled me. Then I'd wonder where I'd been and mentally check my surroundings. My brothers were still asleep in the back seat, the car still droned, the stars still blazed, and the yellow centerline lay perpetually straight ahead, just beyond reach of the headlights.

I began to see things, or, in an attempt to create stimulus, my mind did. It was like sitting by a waterfall for a while and your mind begins to detect or create patterns, beats, or even melodies from the white noise of the falling water.

Only these creations were visual. At first, large, dark shapes formed in the void beyond the full cast of the headlights. I thought they might be cattle or even pronghorn standing in the shadows. Without turning the car and the headlights in their direction, I couldn't get enough of a look to tell, and I was sure that they'd disappear if I did, but slowing my progress or waking up my brothers wasn't an option.

Then the shapes moved to the edge of the headlight beams, and I could tell from their profiles they were horses. Their erect stance indicated curiosity. I was seeing them now on fairly regular intervals. I'd see one and, in what seemed like a few minutes later, I'd get a feeling that another would be appearing soon, which it did. They were still only profiles, but after a spell of how long I couldn't tell they began to move into the beams cast by the headlights, and I saw them in full detail.

They were completely page white, with long, falling tails, plush flowing manes, and white hooves. But their most astonishing feature was their wings, which unfurled in billows of white feathers. The leading edge of each wing was rounded with the incipient curl of breaking surf and the trailing edge was a thundering avalanche. Their primary feathers fingered the night air in slow flurries.

On the edge of the light, they extended their front legs and bowed their heads, all the while eyeing me with a knowing gaze, as if they had planned this appearance. They held a regal expression, assured of their purpose and confident in their role to fulfill it. The world they came from held echelons of creatures, each with its own power and position.

Suddenly they were airborne, vaulting the road and the car, their mammoth wings spread in powerful thrusts, gliding to a landing, evaporating into the dark. I never feared a collision, but gazed transfixed, watching them materialize along the headlights' beam, lower their haunches, and launch without effort over the car, into the night.

Throughout this episode, I was only conscious of piloting a vehicle through a three–dimensional night; I had no sensation of a road under me. I was guided by the yellow line vanishing into the distant black and aligned completely with it. There was no sense of sway or of rise and fall, only the sense of flow, like water streaming into the future. I wasn't carried along, but existed as part of the current. Time and space were no longer separate; both blended into a single experience.

As the eastern sky lightened just perceptibly, the horses began to dim and kept dimming with the brightening horizon. By the time the first sunbeams speared the sky, even before the sun itself appeared, they vanished altogether. Roadside plant silhouettes formed in the gloaming, and assumed full dimension with sunrise. I found myself once again in a car, on a deserted highway, headed east into the soft glow of dawn.

With the fading of the horses, I was suddenly very sleepy, as if my mind had been overtaxed with their creation and needed to recharge. As beautiful as the sunrise was, I began to nod off, snapping back to attention when my chin slammed my chest. I struggled to stay conscious and attentive and was about to pull over to sleep when I saw a sign indicating that West Yellowstone was only a few miles ahead. I pulled into a gas station; neither brother stirred. I got gas and a coffee, drove through the unoccupied entrance gate of Yellowstone National Park, and, without a map, wandered deserted park roads looking for a campground. When I passed a sign stating that the nearest campground was farther than I thought I could drive, I drove to the next gravel pullout, parked, and stilled the engine. The sudden, vast silence rang in my ears.

Tim and Ben were still asleep. I intended to grab a sleeping bag from the trunk and lie down under the nearby trees for a while. Instead, I opened the car door, took two steps toward the trunk, and slumped to the ground, face down, arms at my sides, out cold. I had driven for 15 hours, 780 miles. When the guys woke me two hours later, I had marble-sized chunks of gravel embedded in my cheeks and lips.

Chapter 34

My brothers' plan was to get some breakfast and find the fishing. We quickly fixed a pot of oatmeal, followed by tea, and found the Madison River, which already had a number of anglers along the shore. One of them, noticing we had no licenses, warned us in a friendly way about the presence of plainclothes rangers, who posed as fishermen in order to get close enough to determine if an angler had a license or not. We thanked him for the heads up, drove down the road looking for a less crowded spot, and found one where the river split to pass an island. A maintenance crew was pulling weeds from the still water behind a dam. Schools of trout finned or cruised the flat water, some of them shockingly large. Tim and Ben began casting to these fish but couldn't draw a strike.

Repeated attempts, with different tackle, proved no more effective. This was the most fish we'd seen since Alaska, and their disinterest, compared with the ease with which we'd drawn strikes up north, was frustrating. It was an odd situation to be able to see so many trout in one small area, akin to a view of finning goldfish in a backyard garden pool. No one from the crew said anything to us about the trout or the weeds or the fact that we were fishing without licenses. I shuffled back to the car, fell asleep, and missed the next act in the continuing drama of our unsportsmanlike conduct.

While I slept in the back of the car, Tim and Ben drove to another stretch of water. There anglers lined the banks. Signs everywhere listed the rules governing the fishing, among them the need for a license, the release of all fish, and the use of a single barbless hook. The fish were holding beneath a bridge, on the downstream side, and, after the earlier frustration with fish he could see, Tim decided to improve his chances with a treble hook. Not only were treble hooks illegal, but snagging fish with them was also. Which is what he proceeded to do, lowering the treble hook under the fish and yanking it upward to "snag" the trout. This motion pretty obviously gives itself away, alerting those nearby to what is going on. Tim had just snagged a sizable trout and, while struggling to land it, was approached by a nearby "angler" who revealed his ranger badge and asked Tim for his license.

Witnessing all this from nearby, Ben later said that the first things he worried about were: how much is the fine and will they confiscate our rods? He strolled over to learn what was transpiring, and the ranger noticed that he didn't have a license either and detained him also. They had to follow the ranger in their car to the station, where the ranger issued the citations.

Inside the office, Ben had his first question answered: he got a written warning for fishing without a license, Tim a $35 fine for the same, as well as for using a treble hook and for snagging trout. This paper work took time to complete, with Tim and Ben providing identity and the ranger dutifully explaining what they were being charged with, as well as informing them of their due process rights. He was seated at his desk with the completed paperwork turned so they, leaning over the front of the desk, could read it and follow his explanation.

As he walked them through the fine print, pointing out with his pen the important clauses within the citations, Tim's nose suddenly began to bleed. Large drops of blood fell onto the documents, splattering in a large radius, then surged to a near-steady stream, covering the desk blotter and spraying the nearby calendar, clock, file folders, and book ends. Tim quickly attempted to staunch the flow, first with his cupped hand, which overflowed, and then with his sweatshirt sleeve held to his nose. The ranger jumped to his feet, eyes agog, and rifled through all the desk drawers looking for tissue to no avail, mumbling, "What the hell…" Ben stood, mouth agape, silent in utter disbelief. As the bloody flow continued, Tim stepped away from the desk, gushing all over the floor. He looked for a sink without success, and then sidestepped toward the door with Ben and the ranger following.

"We're done here," the ranger stated flatly. "I suggest you both purchase licenses and fish legally from now on. You're free to leave."

At the car, Tim and Ben rooted around for, and found, a dirty sock, which Tim used to absorb the now lighter blood flow. I slept on. Holding the sock to his nose and driving with the other hand, Tim honked through his nasal cavities to no one, "But sir, I didn't even get to pay the fine."

"Yeah," Ben agreed. "And we've still got our rods."

That's when I woke up and got the whole story enthusiastically amplified. Tim's nose eventually dried up without a clue as to why it started to bleed, and it was time to find a campsite and regroup. After roaming from one full campground to the next, we finally found an available campsite and set up camp. A trip to town for beer was in order, so we stocked up and returned to fix a meal and discuss our situation.

Over canned chili and rice we discovered that we had $84 left among us. It was time to head home. But the direct route home, I–80, ran due east from where we were, north of Grand Teton National Park and Rocky Mountain National Park, which we wanted to see. So we compromised and charted a route further south, swinging through the parks and then back northeast to join I–80. It was out of our way, but not by much. We figured the money would last if we kept moving. It would be a hurried tour through the parks, but at least we'd get to see them from the car, and the route offered the remote possibility that we might even get to fish.

Rising early the next morning, Tim drove through the southern third of Yellowstone along the Rockefeller Parkway into Grand Teton National Park. Traffic filled the main road and the scenic view pull–offs. Crowds formed at every moose or bison sighting, backing up traffic. A constant stream of cars filed into and out of each campground. By mid–morning signs read "full." Motor homes, trucks towing trailers or boats, and pickups with campers formed long lines on both the highway and parked alongside it. Throngs of hikers gathered at trailheads, and parking lots at the visitor center and general store were crammed.

Through the bottlenecks, traffic halted. Ferry service across Jenny Lake was booked, as were all ranger–guided hikes and presentations. Ranger programs and park lodging were available with reservations only.

The lure of the open road was buried under the swarming

hordes. The parks, made easily accessible with highways and bus tours, comfortable with facilities and attractive ranger programs, were being loved to death.

With these mobs, driving without stopping seemed the sensible choice, even if it was to another national park. Finding a parking space, never mind solitude, was going to involve more preparation than we had time for. We hoped that Rocky Mountain National Park would somehow be less crowded.

Tim drove south to Rock Springs, then east and south again across the sagebrush flats of Colorado, where we gassed up in Craig. From Craig, it was only 120 miles to the western entrance of the park near Grand Lake, so we pressed on, arriving in Grand Lake around 1:00 a.m. In a parking place, we prepared a luscious feast of peanut butter sandwiches and cocoa and fell asleep on the sidewalk. After driving nearly 600 miles to avoid crowds, the irony of sleeping on Main Street completely escaped us.

I woke to the sound of people stepping around me, shocked by the memory of where I was. I rustled my brothers, and we scrambled to our feet, laced up our boots, and stowed the sleeping bags in the car. Just down the road, we found the west entrance to the park. Right away, we crossed the Colorado River near its headwaters, which gather in a horseshoe basin rimmed on three sides by the Continental Divide. The west and north sides of the watershed are defined by ten peaks over 12,000 feet. There are over 60 such peaks within the park's 415 square miles. The main auto road we were on, the Trail Ridge Road, was built by the CCC in the 1930s. At 48 miles, it is the highest continually paved highway in the U.S.

Just after cresting the divide itself, we passed the highest point on the road, at 12,183 feet, higher than anywhere we'd been on foot. We'd left our adventure land in the Pacific watershed and were drawn eastward from now on by the gravitational pull of the Atlantic, where our home rivers emptied. We drove slowly, but not just because the winding road required it. This would be our last visit to the big mountains and the glaciers, snowfields, and rivers that they spawned. Once we broke open into the grassland and sagebrush of the plains, our adventure would become just a long drive home.

So, at a fork, where one way would keep us in the park just a little longer, we took it. We'd hiked, fished, camped, and adventured in wild mountain land for so long that it was hard to leave it. We pulled out at every scenic viewpoint, got out of the car, and just let our eyes roam. It was the slowest 50 miles we ever drove. We left the park at Beaver Meadows and dropped down to the town of Estes Park, where we lingered over the treat of a diner breakfast.

We left a tip as big as we thought we could manage and, stepping into the sunshine, counted our remaining funds. Seventy dollars would have to get us 2,000 miles. That meant a continued peanut butter and oatmeal diet, which I already looked upon with nostalgia. With the adventure behind us, the camping diet of our wandering was the last remaining strand connecting us to our journey, parts of which already seemed like a long time ago.

Chapter 35

With what was left of the afternoon, we drove east on I–76 to Fort Morgan, pulled off, and found a campground on the sagebrush flats. We ate a canned dinner, heated over the gas stove, built a fire, and spent the next couple of hours staring at the stars or gazing at the embers. Both were mesmerizing. We had little to say. When we spoke, it was in low voices. The embers faded to ashes. We doused the fire and crawled into our bags, mumbling our good nights.

I stared up at the night, radiant with stars trying to preserve their identity by outshining the full moon. Between them, the earth was bathed in soft, clear light. Even the smallest branches of the sagebrush stood out. The deluge of details from every perspective rivaled the stars in number, as if each twig and blade of grass, wrapping itself in the abundant light, welcomed the gift from the heavens. An inviting, comfortable earth slept peacefully.

My back ached from too much sitting in the car, so I quietly pulled myself from my bag, laced my boots, and walked out onto the sagebrush flat, hoping movement would relieve the pain. We'd be home in a few days, the questions about my future haunted me, and it was time for a reckoning.

We'd been given much precisely because we'd reached for

much. Through our passions and exertions, we'd put ourselves in places we'd never see again, met people who befriended us in ways that humbled us, and endured trials that provided rewards we'd gain no other way. At times we'd behaved far beneath the standards that the natural world's grandeur inspired. Yet, despite these shortcomings, we'd found rescue and restoration in unlimited supply. Wilderness is the one place where the same rules apply to all species, humans included. As such, we need to be reminded of them and be governed by them from time to time to remember what we're just a part of.

I had been trying to think my way logically through my future, seeking a hidden door that would open and reveal what I'd been unable to find, believing that if only I could find the correct line of thought I would find the answer.

What I realized, pacing through that star-spangled night, was that it wasn't a question of finding, or even choosing, the one right path but rather that the path would form itself from the decisions I made every day, every hour, every moment. My actions would create my self rather than find it, and so I would come to inhabit it and it me. To give yourself to the world, to lose yourself in the world, is the only way to define yourself. You write your life as you live it. Enlarging interest, moving your center of focus from yourself to the world, merging your lonely "self" with the wondrous, never lonely whole. This is what it means to live well.

By this time, I'd been awake for a few hours, walking the sagebrush under the moon. The eastern horizon revealed a bare fringe of light, triggering a memory of predawn light on the river as a boy and the enchantment it brought. And then I realized that the river had already shown me the way forward.

At that hour, no one is around. The fish have rested from at least the night before. The stream, cloaked in early morning dim, holds fish less wary, more receptive. These elements combine to raise anticipation, which heightens focus, which, in turn, raises the chances of losing yourself. You begin to see possibilities more frequently, perhaps because your normally fixed alignment with perception goes fluid, recognizing openings unseen before.

Lost in the present, you attain a sort of altered consciousness in which time may or may no longer be linear. It expands or contracts or even stands still. The drifting fly, the follow of the rod, the ever-so-slight tension in the sweep of the cast, mirrored by the murmur and gurgle of the water, the ratchet call of the kingfisher, the whistle of the strafing merganser, all combine to impart a tingling, anticipatory energy. In a sense, you're more in the trout's world than in your own. This not only feels comfortable, but also feels right, like it's where you belong—to the world.

That same memory of the river before dawn recalled the feeling I had on opening day of trout season—that it was the one day each year that Ben and Tim and I were brothers together. And I remembered again how much this trip, for me, was an attempt to recapture that. Instead, the trip had revealed the differences between us, which were too great to ignore.

Those opening days on the river together had been our collective and proprietary claim on our lives, separate from the adults who had violated that claim. My hope to unify us, as noble as it was, faded as the trip progressed. Over the past two months, we had driven over 13,000 miles, through seven provinces and 14 states. We were still acting in consort, but the commitment beyond our daily activities had been lost to the intervening years. We couldn't take that connection with us, nor could we grow with it into the people we would become. That connection was too distant, like the memory of life before a war, following which the new order assumes a shape we now must adapt to as the former life fades. We were old friends fallen out of touch, who have changed in different directions and upon reacquaintance find themselves estranged. The fracture has changed everything.

My hope for this journey was to restore our former connections and foster their growth into our futures together. But traveling together has a way of determining its own meaning, and this adventure, despite my sincerest wishes, was no different. Instead of a hail to our future as adults together, it stood as a tribute to our past, sufficient in its own right but unsuited for the changes we'd be facing in adulthood.

The fringe of light on the eastern horizon had now become a narrow band, silhouetting a freight train running south to north. I stopped walking and counted 189 cars in a rhythmic two-count beat, drifting through the strands of memories.

At some point while counting, the thought occurred to me that I fish because I need what the natural world teaches me when I'm on the river, in the forest, early in the morning: patience, observation, perseverance, ingenuity, intuition, reflection, insight, and, yes, even wisdom. All senses are alive to the pressure of the current, the purling of the moving water, the birdsong, the transcendent whiff of the wild azalea and the mossy aroma at the border of river and shore, the glint of the reflection on the water's surface and the depth without floor of the water holding trout. I am connected to everything else, and at home with myself as part of that larger world.

The one dimension I've omitted is time. Seeing myself as the 12–year–old, the 21–year–old, and now, the 69–year–old, still on the river, fly–fishing for trout, I see my selves over the chronology of my life—who I was, how I've changed, who I might become with the cultivation of grace and compassion. The man in the river, over time, has evolved to a point where there is part of the river in the man, with the hope that it will become even more so, until the man and the river are one.

Acknowledgements

Over the years since this trip I've told friends some of the stories that came from it and they often suggested that I write a book about it. I thank them for urging me, and hope they enjoy the result.

I would like to thank my supportive family members for their encouragement over the years. Thanks to our two sons, Graham and Kelsey for their support and observations. And thanks to Ben and Tim, my brothers, for their interest and help. Thanks to Tamsen, our departed sister, for her appreciation.

Many thanks to the whole Wild Branch Writing Workshop team: to the instructors, the staff and to my writers group.

Thank you to Peter Hughes, for his generosity and friendship. His assistance came at just the right time.

I am very grateful to readers of early drafts for their support and perceptive guidance. Thank you, Annie Wanderman, Kay Abella, and Barry Huber.

I am greatly indebted to June Fiorelli, author of published prose and poetry, for her expert writing help and for her heartfelt support. Thanks to June's daughter, Annie, for her encouragement.

Many thanks to David Dvorkin, who designed and formatted the interior of the book and designed the cover. His patience with my many questions and knowledge of what would work best for the book is greatly appreciated.

My thanks to Margaret Miner for her suggestion that I contact Suzi Arensberg.

Thank you to Suzi Arensberg Diacou, for her insightful editing suggestions and superb copy editing. This is a much better book because of her attention.

Special thanks to Larry Herrick for his friendship, careful reading, and his perceptive comments.

Most of all, I am grateful to my wife, Monique, for her devout support and steadfast partnership in all the adventures we share. She has been my number one champion.

CPSIA information can be obtained
at www.ICGtesting.com
Printed in the USA
LVHW082048300320
651633LV00008B/258